RAINBOW RECIPES

Inspired by the many health benefits of The Rainbow Diet

CHRIS WOOLLAMS and BARBARA COX

Rainbow Recipes

First published in October 2015 by Health Issues Ltd

Photography by James Davies of JD Photography
Cover design by Jeremy Baker.

ISBN 978-0-9565391-9-9

Printed in England by
CPI UK
Bumpers Farm, Chippenham, Wiltshire
SN14 6LH

Protect and Correct with Over 100 Ways to 'Eat a Rainbow'

Introduction

Back in July 2008, Chris Woollams first published The Rainbow Diet and showed us that natural compounds are an essential part of any prevention or treatment programme for any disease or ailment. Eating a rainbow diet certainly offers everybody a real opportunity to correct and heal.

The book sold well and had a huge impact on so many, yet Chris felt that he could do way more by showing people some practical ways to incorporate his thinking into their everyday meal planning.

In order to do this Chris has teamed up with award-winning nutritionist Barbara Cox, who writes for **icon** magazine. Barbara has years of experience in making healthy food practical and hassle-free; she founded the healthy meal delivery company, Nutrichef, and works with the sick, the healthy and the super-fit. She creates recipes and meal plans to support patients in fighting cancer; she has delivered hundreds of healthy meals a day to clients all over the UK and also works with elite athletes competing at national, world and Olympic levels.

Barbara now brings her skills to The Rainbow Diet kitchen, determined to create recipes that deliver massive impact as part of the Rainbow Diet philosophy.

Foreword - Chris Woollams

Back in 2004, **Chris Woollams**, a former Oxford University biochemist and then advertising agency chairman, started a personal mission. His 24-year-old daughter, Catherine, had been diagnosed with a malignant glioma and, despite the prognosis being a dire 6 months, had already survived longer than anyone before at the London hospital where she was being treated.

Chris and Catherine were constantly finding out new information from around the world that could help her. But they had a major concern. If the information exists but no one has easy access to it, they are not so much dying of cancer, they are dying of ignorance.

And so the mission started - to provide easy access to this wealth of information in easy-to-understand, and use, ways. A major part, obviously, concerned diet – specifically nutrition and nourishment. Much in demand as a speaker, he started using the phrase *'Eat a Rainbow Diet'* as he toured the world. In 2005 he developed a 'theory'; a theory that became a science-backed Truth.

It's easy to forget that, back in 2004, The Rainbow Diet was a revolutionary theory. Western Health Authorities were pushing a low fat/high carb doctrine; while the media seemingly could not let a week pass without extolling the virtues of a South-East Asian or Chinese diet. But where were the rigour and the research?

Chris based his theory on early research from Harvard Medical School about the benefits of 'colourful Mediterranean diets', but he was also intrigued by 'The French Paradox' - an 'inconvenient truth' that the French ate more fat and drank more alcohol than any other nation but developed less cancer and heart disease. Moreover, he was in Gascony when research executed only in France showed this region to be the epicentre of the paradox. The Gascons ate even more fat – the home of *foie gras* – and drank even more alcohol – the home of Madiran and Armagnac – than anyone else in France, but had even less cancer and heart disease!

Of course, the French Paradox is only a paradox if it runs counter to perceived wisdom – and it did. Health authorities were obsessed by eating a low fat and high carb diet for good health, yet 'low fat / high carbs' was the medical myth lying at the heart of a Western illness epidemic of obesity, diabetes, cancer, heart disease and dementia.

Since 2005 there has been an explosion in research into the Rainbow Diet and its benefits, not just with cancer but with other chronic illnesses. One Harvard study with women aged between 50 and 70 showed that those who adhered most closely to the Rainbow Diet were, by the end of the 15-year research period, completely free of 11 chronic illnesses and 40 per cent more likely to live past 70. Research has also shown genetic effects, for example, in preserving the stability of DNA telomeres. People in research are thus seen to be living longer in full health – the Rainbow Diet benefit is thus *live younger, longer.*

Twelve top doctors even wrote to Prime Minister David Cameron in 2013 imploring him to make the colourful Mediterranean Diet the gold standard in the UK.

What are the main elements of the diet?

An important factor is that refined carbs and empty calories are recognised as bad for you – they drive up oxidative stress and inflammation in the body. And inflammation is the precursor to almost all chronic illness. For example, in both America and the UK, cardiologists are now arguing that without inflammation in the arteries, the 'bad fat' would not 'stick' to the artery walls. Current thinking is that 'saturated fat' is not so bad after all, as long as you keep the balance in your body favouring 'good fat'.

But there is a trump card. The variety of colourful vegetables and fruits isn't merely appetising; it contains a host of bioactive compounds, and research shows the benefits are cumulative and dose-dependent: the more you consume, the healthier you become. For example, some 65 natural compounds are already known from research to have 'Epigenetic benefits'; that is their action can correct flaws that develop around your cells' DNA resulting in a loss of crucial messages. We have all been told that a good diet can 'protect' you; research is showing it can 'correct' you too, when it contains phytonutrients (from plants) such as phenols, carotenoids, anthocyanins, sulforaphanes, indole 3 carbinol, curcumin, resveratrol, EGCG, omega 3, silibinin, citrus pectins, lycopene and many, many more.

So what are the 'rules'?

1. No refined foods or added glucose.
2. Consume 'good fats' like extra virgin olive oil, walnut oil, and nuts and seeds daily.
3. Eat fish at least twice per week.

4. Eat little or no red meat, but instead consume organic chicken or game.

5. Eat a wide variety of colourful fresh vegetables.

6. Eat some colourful fresh fruits but far less in quantity than vegetables.

7. Eat herbs and spices, and consume infusions – teas like green tea.

8. Drink moderate amounts of red wine (one glass per day for women, two for men).

9. Limit cows' dairy, replacing it with a little goats' and ewes' dairy.

10. Drink a plentiful supply of mineral water.

To keep people up to date with the latest research, we have a new website www.the-rainbow-diet.com and a second link via www.eat-a-rainbow.org. You can also reach the recipe section via www.rainbow-recipes.com.

Do I eat it? I try to follow it to the letter. And now, with Barbara's great recipes, it will be even more delicious.

Chris Woollams (October 2015)

Barbara Cox

Chris and I have been writing this cookbook together since 2011. There have been numerous false starts, for a rainbow of reasons, but the time is now right for us to pour our collective energies into The Rainbow Diet Cookbook. Cookbooks, I believe, should not only provide us with ideas and information, they should inspire us, lift our spirits, free our minds and brighten our outlook on life. They influence our choice of meals, and, therefore, the long-term health of our family members. They suggest food to serve to friends at a dinner party, a topic of conversation around the table, and (especially in the case of this book) food for thought afterwards. Cookbooks teach us about other countries and cultures, tempting us to try tantalisingly tasty ingredients that have the potential to positively impact our lives. They also invite the soul to relive memories and experiences of precious moments in our lives. My own passion for cooking with healthy ingredients was greatly influenced while living in Japan, whose people consume a wide variety of vegetables every day, plenty of fish, not much red meat, and very little dairy. It's no coincidence that levels of cancer in Japan are still relatively low.

Research shows that the pigments that give colour to foods (especially brightly-coloured foods) happen to be very important, health-inducing substances called antioxidants. They work by neutralising 'free radicals' - potentially harmful by-products of normal biochemical processes that occur in our bodies each and every day. In this book we start by listing foods (mainly fruit and vegetables) of the seven different colours of the rainbow. Since each colour is caused by different antioxidant pigments, I have created a range of recipes that include foods from each of the lists. Another feature of the book is that most of the recipes begin with a paragraph called 'Featured Ingredient'. This tells you about the range of different nutrients in the featured ingredient, for example whether it's a good source of fibre, protein, essential (healthy) fats, antioxidants, vitamins and minerals. The paragraph also includes a very brief description of just one or two ways in which the human body uses the nutrients in the featured ingredient.

Barbara Cox (October 2015)

Rainbow Foods

Here are a few examples of some rainbow-coloured foods to expect in the recipes and to experiment with on your own.

RED

Acai berries, adzuki beans, apples, beetroot, berries, cherries, cranberries, currants, damsons, goji berries, guava, kidney beans, papaya, pomegranates, plums, radishes, raspberries, red grapefruit, red grapes, red lentils, red peppers, tomatoes, watermelons.

Meats -
organic particularly game

Red Wine -
Cabernet Sauvignon (limited to two or three times a week)

ORANGE

Apricots, cantaloupes, cape gooseberries, carrots, ginger, kumquats, lentils, mandarins, nectarines, oranges, peaches, persimmons (Sharon fruit), saffron, squash blossoms, swedes, sweet potatoes, tangerines, turmeric, yams, yuzu.

YELLOW

Apple cider vinegar, artichokes, bamboo shoots, barley, bean sprouts, buckwheat, burdock, cauliflower, celeriac, chestnuts, chickpeas, coconut, corn, daikon, eggs, elderberries, fish, (particularly oily fish), garlic, honeydew melon, horseradish, lemons, lotus root, lychees, maple syrup, maitake mushrooms, millet, nuts, oats, olive oil, onions, parsnips, pineapples, potatoes, quinoa, raw honey, rutabaga, salsify, seeds, shiitake mushrooms, sprouted beans, star fruit, taro, turnips, yellow peppers.

GREEN	BLUE	INDIGO	VIOLET
Alfalfa, asparagus, artichokes, avocado, broccoli, cabbage, capers, celery, chard, chives, chicory, courgettes, edamame (soya beans), flaxseeds, fennel, green lentils, gooseberries, green beans, green grapes, green tea, herbs, kale, kohl rabi, kiwi, leeks, lemongrass, limes, okra, olives, pak choi, peas, pumpkin seeds, rocket, runner beans, seaweeds, snow peas, spinach, spring onions, sprouted mung beans, sugar snap peas, wakame seaweed, watercress, wasabi, wheatgrass.	Black-eyed peas, blueberries, dulse, hijiki, kombu, laver, nori.	Blackberries, blackcurrants, dates, grapes, juniper.	Aubergine, beetroot, dates, dragon fruit, dark grapes, figs, mangosteen, olives, plums, red onions, shallots.

Contents

(All recipes and nutritional calculations are based on serving suggestions of 4 people per recipe, unless otherwise stated)

KEY: Tsp = teaspoon = 6ml
Tbsp = tablespoon = 18ml

BREAKFASTS

1. Baked apples with nuts and seeds 14
2. Green tea and lemon muffins 15
3. Eggs Florentine with spinach and lemon hollandaise sauce 16
4. Traditional Japanese breakfast of rice, miso soup and salmon 19
5. The ultimate omelette 20
The Basic - 1 base style omelette 20
The Add-Ins – everything you can add to an omelette 20

Juicing

1. Rainbow special 23
2. Mellow yellow 23
3. Green and lean 23
4. Red delight 23
5. True blue 23

Smoothies

1. Apple, avocado and lime 25
2. Tomato and chilli 25
3. Beetroot, orange, ginger and spinach 25
4. Pineapple, papaya, lime and grapefruit 25
5. Nut butter power-up 25
6. Blueberry, almond and cherry 25
7. Blackberry, lemon and coconut water 25
8. Kiwi fruit and banana 26
9. Strawberry and raspberry 26
10. Nectarine and flaxseeds (ground) 26

LUNCHES - Salads

1. Marinated aubergines served with tapas 30
2. Daikon slaw 31
3. Dill-icious potato salad 32
4. Corn and kale salad 33
5. Pineapple and beansprout salad 35
6. Mackerel salad in little gems 36
7. Jewelled rice salad 37
8. Mediterranean quinoa salad 38
9. Lemon and tarragon chicken salad 39
10. The ultimate salad bar 40
A list of mix-and-match salad items to make a variety of salad combos
The Basics – the usual things. 40
The Add-Ins – the not so usual things - everything from seaweeds to satsumas. 40

Dressings and Infused Oils

1. Olive oil and balsamic (with 3 combos) 42
2. Sweet and sour dressing (Japanese style) 42
3. Kiwi and orange dressing 42
4. Ginger dressing 42
5. Fresh herb and coconut oil dressing 42

Soups

1. Sweet potato minestrone 45
2. Lentil and orange 46
3. Barley broth 47
4. Chunky vegetable 48
5. Creamy broccoli 50
6. Borsche 51
7. Broad bean 53
8. Sweet potato and coconut 54
9. Watercress 55
10. Indonesian "Laske" soup with rice noodles and coconut milk 56

Dips

1. Hummous – 1 basic chickpea hummous with 5 different add-in ideas (beetroot, harissa spices, pea, spinach, courgette) 59
2. Baba ganoush – aubergine dip 61
3. Black bean and olive 62
4. Guacamole 62
5. Salmon and dill 63

Herbs and Garnishes

1. Rosemary 64
2. Sage 64
3. Coriander 64
4. Oregano 64
5. Thyme 64
6. Parsley 64
7. Mint 64
8. Basil 64
9. Chives 64
10. Tarragon 64
11. Dill 64

Sandwich Toppings

1. Coronation chicken 66
2. Salmon mousse 67
3. Shrimp, crayfish and lemon 68
4. Shiitake mushroom pâté 69

Sushi Slice

1. Seaweed style sushi sandwich (if you don't think you have the skills to roll sushi!) 71

DINNERS

Poultry

1. Chicken bites with coconut topping 74
2. Duck with cinnamon, star anise and orange glaze 75
3. Chicken with a walnut topping 77

4. Chicken with Thai-style butternut squash and roasted cashews 78
5. Turkey tikka burger 79

Fish

1. Moroccan spiced fishcakes (haddock) 80
2. Mediterranean sea bass 82
3. Salmon in a watercress sauce 83
4. Chilli mussels 84
5. Kedgeree 85

Meat

1. Lamb tagine 87
2. Venison bhuna 88
3. Lamb chilli 89
4. Lamb burgers with fresh mint sauce 90
5. Meatball curry (use either lamb or venison) 91

Vegetarian

1. Falafels 93
2. Caribbean spiced bean burgers 94
3. Brazil nut burgers 95
4. Sweet potato polenta with Asian vegetable fricassee 96
5. Watercress potato cakes with red radish 97
6. Beetroot risotto 98
7. Lentil dahl 100
8. Stuffed squash with shiitake mushroom and beans **101**
9. Thai spiced rice noodles with vegetables 102
10. Millet, carrot & sesame burger 103

The Ultimate Pizza

1. Gluten-free pizza base 104
2. Almond flour pizza base 106
3. Cauliflower pizza base 106
4. Pizza bases 107
5. Pizza toppings 107

Side Dishes

1. Wild rice and millet 108
2. Spring greens with chestnuts 109
3. Red cabbage, onion and apple 109
4. Roasted tomatoes with pesto 110
5. Fennel, pak choi and orange 111
6. Brassicas with garlic 111
7. Brussels sprouts with almonds and pomegranate seeds 112
8. Sweet potato and miso mash 112
9. Chickpea and ginger stew 113
10. Stuffed peppers 113

DESSERTS

1. Sorbet 116
2. Rhubarb with cinnamon crumble 118
3. Chocolate and hazelnut dairy-free ice cream 119
4. Whole fruit popsicles (ice lollies) 120

5. Roasted plums, nectarines and pineapple with rose water   121
6. Red rice pudding with coconut milk   122
7. Cashew and almond butter gluten-free cookies   123
8. Beetroot brownies   125
9. Sweet potato pancakes   126
10. Chia seed pudding   127

Fermented Vegetables

1. Sauerkraut   128

Healthy Barbecuing

Marinades

1. Teriyaki   131
2. Classic BBQ   131
3. Thai sweet chilli   131
4. Satay   131
5. Moroccan   131
6. Chinese 5-spice   131
7. Citrus and herb   132
8. Tandoori   132
9. Honey mustard   132

Snacks

1. Curly kale chips   133
2. Popcorn – 5 variations   134
3. Nachos – 5 variations   135
4. Devilled eggs – 5 variations   136
5. Spiced and toasted nuts and seeds   137

Understanding and using the Rainbow Diet

The Rainbow Diet and Lifestyle   138
The Rainbow Diet and Olive Oil   139
The Rainbow Diet and Alcohol   140
The Rainbow Diet and Spices   142
The Rainbow Diet and Fibre   144
The Rainbow Diet and Pulses   145
The Rainbow Diet and Cows' Dairy   146
The Rainbow Diet and Glutamine   147
The Rainbow Diet and Cholesterol   148
The Rainbow Diet and Epigenetics   149
The Rainbow Diet and Fish   150
The Rainbow Diet and Flaxseed   151
The Rainbow Diet and Supplements   153
Portion Distortion   154
Storage and Freezing   155
The Organic vs Non-Organic Story   156

Food Diaries   158

The Rainbow Diet FAQs   160

About the Authors   164

CANCERactive   167

Index   168

BREAKFAST

"All happiness depends on a leisurely breakfast."

John Gunther

Nutritionists have long said that breakfast is the most important meal of the day, citing studies that find that people who skip breakfast are more likely to have problems with concentration, metabolism and weight. It's good for your body and good for your soul. Breakfast gets your metabolism moving.

Our breakfast ideas combine some of the simplest and easiest-to-prepare natural ingredients. We've also added a couple you'll need to prepare in advance. Incidentally, our Green tea and lemon muffins also make a great healthy snack!

Eggs have had their critics over the years, yet they remain one of the most nutritious foods money can buy. They are a natural source of many nutrients, including high quality protein, vitamins and minerals, particularly B vitamins. Egg yolk is a good source of folic acid.

1. Baked Apples with Nuts and Seeds

A simple breakfast that can be pre-prepared and popped in the oven in the morning or even the night before. The combination of fruit, nuts and seeds makes an ideal breakfast, delivering a healthy injection of vitamins, minerals and energy to keep you going through the morning.

Featured ingredient: apples

Apples are a source of fibre (important for cleansing the colon) and they contain useful quantities of phytonutrients including flavonoids (such as quercetin), vitamin C and beta-carotene. These phytochemicals have an antioxidant effect that helps protect body cells from disease (including cancer). The prefix 'phyto-' actually means plant, but, given the nature of their role, these vital nutrients could just as easily be named 'fighto-chemicals'!

Ingredients:
4 apples (1 apple per person)
50g sunflower seeds
50g pumpkin seeds
50g chopped walnuts
1 tsp ground cinnamon

Nutritional analysis per 220g serving: Calories 314 cals, Fat 19.9g (saturated fat 2.1g), Total Carbs 31.6g (sugar 19.6g, fibre 7.1g), Protein 9.2g

Method:
1. Pre-heat the oven to 180°C.
2. Core each apple through the centre to make a "well" to pour in the seed and nut mixture.
3. Mix the sunflower seeds, pumpkin seeds and walnuts.
4. Stand the apples side by side on a baking tray and pour the mixture evenly into each apple.
5. Bake in the oven for 20-30 minutes until apples are soft.

2. Green Tea and Lemon Muffins with an Apricot Centre

These delicious muffins are great for a breakfast on-the-go, snack, pre- or post-workout or dessert.

Featured ingredient : green tea

Green tea is an excellent source of powerful disease-fighting flavonoids, in particular a group called catechins. Research shows that these phytochemicals are effective at stopping oxidative damage to our cells and that daily consumption of green tea may reduce the risk of a variety of cancers including breast, bladder, colon, lung and oesophagus.

Ingredients:

600g buckwheat flour

150g rice flour

125ml malt barley extract

3 tbsp ground loose green tea (grind in blender until fine or use matcha green tea powder)

1 tbsp barley grass powder (or another tbsp matcha)

2 tsp baking powder

1 tsp baking soda

150ml plain soya yoghurt

2 lemons, zested

1 tbsp veg oil

250ml apple juice

1 whole dried apricot per muffin (12-15 depending on how many muffins)

Method:

1. Preheat oven to 180°C.
2. In a large bowl whisk together buckwheat flour, rice flour, ground tea, barley grass powder, baking powder and baking soda.
3. In a small bowl whisk together the yogurt, oil, lemon zest, malt barley extract.
4. Add the wet ingredients to the dry ingredients and mix well.
5. Divide into muffin cups or moulds.
6. Place 1 apricot in the centre of each muffin.
7. Bake for 12-15 minutes until firm and golden.
8. Cool on a rack.

Nutritional analysis per 78g serving: Calories 185 cals, Fat 1.5g (saturated fat 0g), Total Carbs 39.2g (sugar 3.5g, fibre 4.3g), Protein 6.1g

3. Eggs Florentine with Spinach and Lemon Hollandaise Sauce

A firm weekend favourite at our house and we also like to add smoked salmon, shiitake mushrooms or grilled peppers.

Featured ingredient: spinach

Most of us are aware that spinach is a good source of iron, which is essential for carrying oxygen around our body, but Popeye's favourite food also provides us with other minerals including manganese (for healthy teeth and bones) and magnesium (vital for healthy nerves and muscles). Spinach is an excellent source of vitamin K (which helps our blood clot when we cut ourselves), vitamin A (for seeing in the dark and for healthy skin) and vitamin C (an antioxidant that plays a key role in fighting illness). Other antioxidants found in spinach include a flavonoid called apigenin and a carotenoid called neoxanthin.

Ingredients:
1 kg spinach
8 eggs
1 tsp apple cider vinegar
1 tsp coconut oil
A pinch of pepper
A pinch of Himalayan crystal salt

Method:
1. Crack the eggs, then whisk and set aside.
2. Place a tbsp of water in a pan and wilt the spinach.
3. Place the coconut oil and apple cider vinegar in a hot frying pan.
4. Pour in the egg mixture and fold until semi-cooked.
5. Add the spinach and keep folding until eggs and spinach are fully cooked.
6. Season with salt and pepper.

Lemon Hollandaise Sauce
3 egg yolks
1 cup dairy-free margarine
½ lemon, juiced
1 tbsp hot water
½ tsp Himalayan crystal salt

Method:
1. Melt the butter in a saucepan and then set aside.
2. Place the yolks, lemon juice, hot water and salt into blender and blend until smooth.
3. Slowly blend in the melted butter until the mixture starts to thicken – about 2-3 minutes.
4. Set aside to pour over eggs.

Nutritional analysis per 340g serving: Calories 193 cals, Fat 10.9g (saturated fat 3.9g), Total Carbs 9.8g (sugar 1.7g, fibre 5.5g), Protein 18.2g

4. The Japanese Breakfast – Rice, Miso Soup and Salmon

After living in Japan for almost 10 years, I became accustomed to this nutritious and delicious way to start the day. I absolutely loved the food of Japan, and I've noticed a lot of similarities with the Mediterranean Diet, that paved the way for this book. For example, both diets favour a wide variety of vegetables, nuts and beans. The recipe here is one that I adapted from a friend and followed nearly every day.

Featured ingredient: miso paste

Miso is comprised mainly from soybeans, which are a source of powerful cancer-fighting antioxidants. Research on the health benefits of miso has been carried out at various Japanese universities, for example Shizuoka University, where the most powerful antioxidants of miso were found to be daidzein, genistein and alpha-tocopherol.

Ingredients:
1 tsp white miso per person
1 salmon fillet (100g) per person
450g brown rice or red rice
1 tsp per person dried seaweed
2 spring onions - chopped
1 umeboshi pickled plum per person

Method:
1. Start the rice according to the instructions below.
2. In a pan of boiling water, add 1 tsp miso paste per person. Add the seaweed and simmer for 10 minutes then add the chopped spring onion.
3. In a small skillet pan, fry the salmon fillet until thoroughly cooked.
4. Arrange rice, miso soup and fish on separate plates.

Making the perfect steamed rice:
1. First rinse the rice under running water and then put it in a large pan and cover with cold water. Leave to soak for at least half an hour.
2. Drain the rice and discard the soaking water. Put rice in a large pan containing 585ml clear water.
3. Bring to the boil, and give it a good stir. Cover tightly and turn the heat down very low. Cook for 25 minutes (28 for brown rice) then take off the heat, but don't take the lid off! Leave for five minutes then fork through to fluff up.

Seaweeds to use: kelp (kombu), hikiji and wakame are the most popular.

Nutritional analysis per 220g serving: Calories 542 cals, Fat 9.2g (saturated fat 1.5g), Total Carbs 86g (sugar 0g, fibre 4g), Protein 28g

5. The Ultimate Omelette

Omelettes are fabulous muscle food! The combinations are so varied that it makes cooking fun and it's easy to create a delicious masterpiece omelette in minutes!

Featured ingredient: eggs

One little egg is packed with several vitamins essential to your health, including vitamin B2 (riboflavin, which helps your body convert food into energy), vitamin B12 (cobalamin, vital for producing red blood cells), vitamin A (retinol, important for your eyesight, and vitamin E (tocopherol, an antioxidant that neutralises disease-causing free radicals). Eggs are also packed with a number of minerals, such as iron (which carries oxygen in the blood), zinc (vital in making DNA) and phosphorus (essential for healthy teeth and bones).

Ingredients for the Basics:

2 eggs

A pinch of pepper

A pinch of Himalayan crystal salt

A pinch of turmeric

Coconut oil for frying

Method:

1. For the perfect omelette, break 2 eggs, whisk and season with pepper, Himalayan crystal salt and a pinch of turmeric. At this stage, you can add any of the Add-Ins (see list below).

2. Melt 1 tsp coconut oil in a fry pan and pour the mixture in the pan.

3. After 10 seconds, draw the edges of the mixture to the middle to ensure an even cooking time.

4. Cook for 1-2 minutes, until golden brown on the bottom and then fold onto a plate.

The Add-Ins – the list of potential ingredient combinations for your omelette is endless. These are our favourites:

Shiitake mushrooms

Mixed peppers

Finely chopped spring onion or red onion

Watercress

Avocado

Smoked salmon

Crab

Tuna

Chopped herbs

Spices like turmeric, cumin, ginger, paprika and saffron

Sun-blushed tomatoes

NOTE: Just add a small handful of your choice and add to the top of the omelette while cooking. Fold the omelette over the ingredients and serve hot.

Juicing

The 'colourful Mediterranean Diet' starts and ends with large amounts of fruit and vegetables, but if you'd like to try an alternative way of getting your vitamins and minerals, why not try juicing? Are you aware of the wonders of juicing and the health benefits you can receive from doing so? There are lots of fantastic recipes and creations that you can put together to suit all tastes, and you can even get the kids involved too! Here are ten very good reasons to try juicing.

1) **Stock up on enzymes** – Fresh juices are very rich in enzymes that help digest your food. A shortage of enzymes means we cannot convert foods into energy or transform carbohydrates, proteins, fats, vitamins and minerals into what we need for healthy tissue such as muscle, bone, skin, and so on.

2) **Load up on essential nutrients** – Fresh juicing supplies the vitamins and minerals we need in abundance. And by using a wide variety of vegetables and fruit, you will derive benefit from the myriad of bioactive natural compounds contained. Remember – the benefits are dose-dependent, and juices are a great way of increasing that intake!

3) **Boost your 'wellness'** – Fresh raw juicing has been used by a variety of nutrition experts such as Dr. Max Gerson and the Hippocrates Institute. Both believe patients recover from degenerative illnesses more quickly when put on a diet made largely from fresh raw juices. A study by *Huber et al* in 2003 showed that a one week juice fast reduced LDL cholesterol and normalised insulin levels. And The Rainbow Diet argues that saturated fat per se, is not bad provided the balance of fat is towards good fat.

4) **Eliminate toxins** – Fresh fruit and vegetable juices are a must for all detox diets. Some juices have the ability to rid the body of waste and bacteria, and to deep-cleanse the body.

5) **Get plenty of chlorophyll** – Chlorophyll can be found in abundance in all green plants. It cleanses your digestive system and builds blood cells – making it an all-round great tonic. Alfalfa, wheatgrass, watercress and leafy greens are all high in chlorophyll and are fantastic in juices.

6) **Reduce your risk of premature disease** – this can be aided by the antioxidants contained in juices. Beauty, like health, comes from within so what we eat plays a vital role. Antioxidants are thought to be the secret to living longer and looking younger as they 'mop up' harmful molecules known as 'free-radicals'.

7) **Get your essential amino acids** – These are the building blocks of protein and are vital in the process of digestion and assimilation of food. Fresh raw juices are rich in amino acids and are in an easily digestible form.

8) **Balance acid/alkaline levels** – Western diets tend to be high in salt and sugar. By keeping to an 80% vegetable to fruit ratio, you will flood your body with potassium and magnesium at the expense of sodium and common glucose, resulting in more alkaline and efficient cells – especially important with the immune system.

9) **Aid weight reduction** – juices are both 'filling' and yet low in calories. They help curb the appetite and are, therefore, an important part of many weight loss programmes.

10) **Enjoy all the tastes!** – Try to be creative and try some of the recipes below. They all taste great and will awaken the taste-buds.....so why not get juicing?!

Rainbow Special
1 carrot (unpeeled, topped and tailed), 1 red apple (Gala or Cox), 1 beetroot (skinned and washed but leave the roots and tops on). (A real immune-boosting drink!)
This juice will be high in Vitamin A, C, calcium, magnesium, potassium and iron.

Mellow Yellow
¼ wedge lemon (unwaxed), 2-3 Golden Delicious apples. Juice and serve over crushed ice. This will be a good cleanser and the lemons will have an alkalising effect. Surprisingly, although lemons have an acid taste, after being processed by your digestive system, they have an alkalising effect on the body.

Lean and Green
1 apple, 1 stick of celery (with the leaves), 100g spinach (fresh young leaves), 1 small bunch of watercress, 1 small bunch of wheatgrass (if desired). This will be rich in Vitamins A, C, folic acid and Riboflavin (B2).

Red Delight
4 large tomatoes, 1 carrot (topped and tailed), 1 stick of celery (with the leaves), 1 handful of basil. Add the juice of half a squeezed lemon at the end. This juice will be rich in iron, magnesium and lycopene.

True Blue
100g blueberries, 1 mango (peeled & stoned), 1 pear, 100g red grapes. This juice will be high in antioxidants and will chase away the blues!

Smoothies

Smoothies benefit us in a different way from juices because smoothies contain the whole fruit, not just the juice. This means that smoothies contain the fibrous matter of the fruit and are good sources of fibre, as well as a great way to supercharge our intake of vitamins and minerals.

Blend these smoothies in a food processor or a smoothie maker.

Apple, Avocado and Lime

Peel 1 apple, 1 avocado and juice from 1 lime. Blend with 4 ice cubes and 50ml water.

Tomato and Chilli

Chop 2 tomatoes, 1 stick celery, juice of 1 lemon, dash tabasco sauce and Worcestershire sauce. Add 50ml water and blend until smooth.

Beetroot, Orange, Ginger and Spinach

Add 1 cooked beetroot, 1 orange (peeled and sliced), grate in 1tsp fresh ginger, handful of spinach. Add 50ml water and blend until smooth.

Pineapple, Papaya, Lime and Grapefruit

Add 1 chopped papaya, juice of 1 lime, 1 pink grapefruit, a quarter of a pineapple. Add 50ml water and blend until smooth.

Nut Butter Power-Up

50ml almond milk or coconut milk, 2 tsp cashew nut butter (or another nut butter), 1 banana. Blend until smooth.

Blueberry, Almond and Cherry

Add 50ml almond milk, 50g blueberries, 50g fresh pitted cherries. Blend until smooth.

Blackberry, Lemon and Coconut Water

Add 50g blackberries, juice of 1 fresh lemon, 100ml coconut water. Blend until smooth.

Kiwi Fruit and Banana
Add 2 chopped kiwi and 1 banana to 100ml water. Blend until smooth.

Strawberry and Raspberry
Add 50g strawberries and 50g raspberries to 100ml water. Blend until smooth.

Nectarine and Flaxseeds (ground)
Add 2 peeled nectarines to 100ml water. Add 1tsp ground flaxseeds and blend until smooth.

Add-Ins:
You can add in a variety of extra ingredients to bulk the smoothie into more of a meal. A few ideas to try:

1. Add a scoop of your favourite protein powder (pea, hemp and rice protein powders work well for everyone)
2. Powdered green tea (matcha), or barley grass
3. Bee pollen
4. Liquid chlorophyll
5. Liquid supplements
6. Powdered supplements, including powdered probiotics
7. Dairy-free yogurts
8. Oats – make sure your blender blade can grind the oats!
9. Aloe Vera juice
10. Oils – coconut oil, flaxseed oil, borage oil, black cumin seed oil

Special Note –
These can all be made in larger batches and frozen into ice-lolly moulds then stored in the freezer. You can also freeze smaller amounts in ice cube trays and add smoothie ice cubes to plain water.

Other Fruits to add:
Watermelon, pomegranate, guava, physallis, peach, Sharon fruit, dragon fruit or star fruit.

Featured ingredient: berries

Berries and aggregate fruits like blackberries, raspberries and strawberries are among the healthiest foods on the planet. Rich with colourful pigments (especially anthocyanins) they are a great source of phytochemicals – naturally occurring chemicals which help to neutralise harmful free radicals. Free radicals are by-products of normal biochemical processes that take place in each and every one of us. They are actually utilised by the body to kill bacteria and fight inflammation, but, when they build up to excessive levels, they may begin to damage protein, DNA, cells and tissue through a process called oxidation.

LUNCH

"Ask not what you can do for your country, ask what's for lunch."

Orson Welles

(I guess you can do a lot more for your country if you've had a good lunch!)

Whether you're on the go or at home or on holiday, it's important to get the right fuel in at lunch to keep you going and ward off that afternoon energy dip. Our lunch recipes have been created to fuel your afternoon.

Forget take-out for lunch and think take-in—our lunch solutions can be eaten at home or easily be taken to the office, to school or anywhere else you need to go. Tasty and healthy, these recipes emphasise lots of delicious fresh produce, whole grains and lean protein to fuel you for the rest of your day so you won't feel deprived.

1. Marinated Aubergine Served with Tapas

With everyone's busy schedule, planning meals can be a bore, but these quick and easy aubergine nuggets can keep in the fridge for a few days and be served with salad, bread, rice, pasta or grilled meat and fish.

Featured ingredient: aubergines
Aubergines (otherwise known as eggplants) get their lovely deep blue-purple colour from a pigment called anthocyanins – a group of phytochemicals that help to fight cancer, inflammation and the effects of aging. Aubergines also contain good amounts of various B vitamins including B1, B3, B5 and B6, all of which are involved in extracting energy from our food.

Ingredients:
1 aubergine cut into chunks
1 tbsp olive oil
1 lemon (juice and zest)
1 tsp balsamic vinegar
20g pine nuts
A pinch of Himalayan crystal salt
A pinch of pepper
A pinch of fresh rosemary
Optional – Add poppy seeds, crushed nori seaweed or mint

Method:
1. Brush aubergine chunks with olive oil and grill on high for 10 minutes.
2. Make marinade of olive oil, lemon juice, vinegar, pine nuts and seasoning. Mix well.
3. Place hot aubergines in a bowl and pour over marinade. Stir until coated.
4. Cool and serve without the liquid.

Nutritional analysis per147g serving: Calories 98 cals, Fat 7.2g (saturated fat 0.7g), Total Carbs 8.7g (sugar 3.3g, fibre 5g), Protein 2g

2. Daikon Slaw

This fresh slaw is wonderful either on its own or with a soup, salad or sandwich. Perfect for a picnic!

Featured ingredient: daikon
(also known as mouli)
There's an old Chinese proverb: "Eating pungent radish and drinking hot tea, let the starved doctors beg on their knees!" There's no doubt that doctors wouldn't have so many patients to see if we all ate more radishes and drank tea, especially green tea. Daikon is a Japanese radish and, like other members of the brassica family (including cabbage and cauliflower), they are a good source of various disease-fighting phytochemicals including isothiocyanates and indoles.

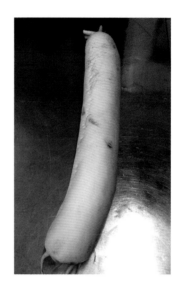

Ingredients:
1 daikon
2 carrots
¼ white or red cabbage
1 red apple
50g walnuts
¼ grated red onion
50ml plain dairy-free yogurt or mayonnaise
1 lemon (juice and zest)
A pinch of pepper
A pinch of Himalayan crystal salt
A pinch of turmeric
Optional – Add sprouted beans or seeds (see sprouted seed section).

Method:
1. Grate the daikon, carrot, cabbage and onion and place in a bowl.
2. Chop the apple and add to grated vegetables.
3. Mix the dairy-free plain yogurt or mayonnaise with seasoning and lemon juice and rind.
4. Mix all ingredients together.
5. Serve with grilled meat, fish or sprouted seeds.

Nutritional analysis per 133g serving:
Calories 165 cals, Fat 11.6g (saturated fat 1g), Total Carbs 14.1g (sugar 7.5g, fibre 2.9g), Protein 3.6g

3. Dill-icious Potato Salad

When I was young, my mother made the best potato salad with dill in the summer when friends came over. My Mum used to add hard-boiled eggs to her potato salad to make it more substantial to fuel our activities. Making memories with great food is so special!

Featured ingredient: dill
Dill is a perennial herb with a distinctive aniseed flavour. It's an excellent source of two antioxidant vitamins that are key players in fighting cancer: vitamins A and C. In fact, a 100g portion of dill provides our entire daily requirement of these two essential nutrients. Dill is also a source of various important minerals, including calcium and manganese (both vital for healthy teeth and bones), iron (a component of haemoglobin, which carries oxygen in our red blood cells) and magnesium and potassium (both essential for healthy nerves and muscles).

Ingredients:
100g potatoes
½ cucumber cut into chunks
50ml plain dairy-free yogurt or mayonnaise
1 tsp Dijon mustard
2 stalks chopped celery
25g chopped parsley
1 grated red onion
50g fresh minced dill
50g fresh edamame beans (soya beans)
A pinch of pepper
A pinch of Himalayan crystal salt

Method:
1. Boil or steam the potatoes for 15 minutes until tender but not falling apart. Cool under running cold water. Drain and set aside.
2. Chop the celery, parsley, dill and grate the onion.
3. Mix the plain yogurt or mayo with the Dijon mustard and seasoning.
4. Mix all ingredients together and serve with your choice of protein (chicken, lamb, fish or beans).

Nutritional analysis per 131g serving: Calories 119 cals, Fat 4.9g (saturated fat 0.7g), Total Carbs 18.6g (sugar 3.1g, fibre 3.5g), Protein 3.9g

4. Corn and Kale Salad

This salad is so bright and colourful, it would cheer anyone up! It's great with fish, chicken and falafels!

Featured ingredient: kale
Kale (borecole) gets its deep green colour from the pigment chlorophyll, an important disease-fighting antioxidant as well as a crucial component of photosynthesis - the process by which plants kindly make carbohydrates for us members of the animal kingdom! Kale is also an excellent source of antioxidant vitamins A and C, an extremely good source of vitamin K (vital for blood clotting) and a useful provider of various minerals including manganese, calcium and phosphorus (all needed by our bones and teeth), copper (an antioxidant) and iron (for carrying oxygen in our blood).

Ingredients:
100g sweetcorn (frozen, defrosted)
100g kale – chopped
1 red pepper – chopped
1 yellow pepper – chopped
1 tomato – chopped
½ red onion – sliced very thinly
1 tin chickpeas – drained and rinsed

Dressing:
50ml extra virgin olive oil
20ml balsamic vinegar
A pinch of turmeric
A pinch of pepper
A pinch of Himalayan crystal salt

Method:
1. Defrost the corn.
2. Chop the kale, peppers, tomato and red onion.
3. Make the dressing by blending all ingredients.
4. Mix all together and serve with your protein of choice (fish, lamb, poultry or beans).

Nutritional analysis per 140g serving:
Calories 59 cals, Fat 0.3g (saturated fat 0g), Total Carbs 13.3g (sugar 2.9g, fibre 2.2g), Protein 2.3g

5. Pineapple and Beansprout Salad

Beansprouts and pineapple together is a powerhouse of a combination. We have the crunch, tang, colour and all the nutritional elements to nourish the body.

Featured ingredient: pineapple
Pineapple is an excellent source of vitamin C, which we all know is a key immune-booster, but not so many of us realise is vital in manufacturing collagen – a protein that strengthens our blood, anchors our teeth in place and helps our skin to heal! Pineapple is also a very good source of the mineral manganese (which strengthens our bones and teeth), and an enzyme called bromelain, which is used in treating sprains and strains.

Ingredients:
½ pineapple – sliced into bite-sized chunks
1 pack beansprouts (150g)
1 tomato
1 punnet of mustard cress
50g cashew nuts
Small handful of coriander or parsley

Dressing:
50ml extra virgin olive oil
20ml balsamic vinegar
A pinch of turmeric
A pinch of pepper
A pinch of Himalayan crystal salt

Method:
1. Chop the pineapple and tomato into bite-sized chunks.
2. Mix with beansprouts, coriander and mustard cress.
3. Toss in dressing.
4. Top with cashew nuts.

EXTRA tips with Nuts:
Soak all nuts in vitamin C powder to help remove any possible molds.

Nutritional analysis per 78g serving:
Calories 89 cals, Fat 6.1g (saturated fat 0g), Total Carbs 6.9g (sugar 1.6g, fibre 0.7g), Protein 4g

6. Mackerel Salad in Little Gems

I started doing this recipe as a finger food for the kids at lunch. For some reason they had aversions to using cutlery, at least it wasn't an aversion to healthy food!

Featured ingredient: mackerel
Being an "oily fish" mackerel is an excellent source of essential fatty acids, especially omega-3, which is essential for a healthy cardiovascular system and believed to play a part in battling cancer. Mackerel is also a good source of the antioxidant mineral selenium, as well as coenzyme Q10 – a vitamin-like substance that acts as an antioxidant and plays a vital role in deriving energy from our food.

Ingredients:
150g cooked mackerel (un-smoked)
3 tbsp of plain dairy-free yogurt
1 tsp horseradish
10g sunflower seeds
10g pumpkin seeds
1 lemon (juice and grated zest)
Handful of tarragon – chopped
A few capers
Baby gem lettuce leaves
A pinch of pepper

Method:
1. Crumble the mackerel and stir in seeds.
2. Mix the dairy-free yogurt with horseradish and stir in chopped tarragon, lemon juice and rind and pepper.
3. Mix all together and spoon into little gem lettuce leaves and serve.

Nutritional analysis per 131g serving: Calories 119 cals, Fat 4.9g (saturated fat 0.7g), Total Carbs 18.6g (sugar 3.1g, fibre 3.5g), Protein 3.9g

7. Jewelled Rice Salad

A firm family favourite for when family and friends come over for a buffet. I always make extra to freeze in individual portions for when someone comes home "starving". Though it's normally served cold, my kids love it hot!

Featured ingredient: wild rice

Biologically more similar to grass than rice, this ingredient contains a significant amount of vitamin C, a cancer-combating antioxidant that also stimulates the production of white blood cells - the body's first line of defence against pathogens and microbes. Whereas white rice typically has minimal antioxidant capacity, wild rice contains 20-30 times more antioxidants. The high protein content found in wild rice is also good for the growth and maintenance of our bones and muscles. Proteins are made up of amino acids - the building blocks of life, so wild rice is especially important for vegetarians, as they can sometimes find it a challenge to source enough protein.

Ingredients:
100g brown rice
25g wild rice
2 stalks celery - chopped
25g dried apricots - chopped
25g dried cranberries
1 cucumber - chopped
3 spring onions – sliced thinly
50g peas - frozen
1 pomegranate – separate the seeds first
120g watercress - chopped
1 green pepper - chopped
1 lemon (juice and zest)
25g fresh mint
25g fresh parsley

Dressing:
50ml extra virgin olive oil
20ml balsamic vinegar
A pinch of pepper
A pinch of Himalayan crystal salt
A pinch of turmeric
A pinch of paprika

Method:
1. Boil the rice until fluffy, then set aside to cool.
2. Combine all ingredients and mix thoroughly with dressing.

Nutritional analysis per 171g serving: Calories 121 cals, Fat 1.1g(Saturated fat 0g), Total Carbs 25.3g (sugar 4.7g, fibre 3.9g), Protein 4.1g

8. Quinoa Salad

Quinoa is so easy to prepare, easy to adapt to a savoury or sweet recipe and easy to digest!

Featured ingredient: quinoa
This gluten-free grain from South America is rich in minerals, but has a low glycaemic index, making it an ideal source of energy for people suffering from diabetes. From the point of view of fighting cancer, quinoa provides us with two flavonoids— quercetin and kaempferol. These phytonutrients, which have anti-inflammatory and anti-viral properties, have surprised researchers by having higher amounts of flavonoids than typically high-flavonoid foods like cranberries or lingonberries!

Ingredients:
150g quinoa
50g almonds
50g red grapes - halved
1 red apple - chopped
1 green pepper - chopped
2 stalks celery - chopped

Dressing:
Add a dressing of your choice from the selection below.

Method:
1. Boil the quinoa in water for approx. 15 minutes until tender. Drain, cool.

Nutritional analysis per 146g serving: Calories 250 cals, Fat 8.7g (saturated fat 0.8g), Total Carbs 36.8g (sugar 8g, fibre 6g), Protein 8.4g

9. Lemon and Tarragon Chicken Salad

Tarragon has such a fresh flavour and works beautifully with chicken. You can substitute the chicken for chickpeas and make a vegetarian version too. This salad is perfect in a little gem lettuce leaf or with a slice of rye bread.

Featured ingredient: tarragon
There are different varieties of tarragon depending on where this herb is cultivated. The French kind appears to have a superior taste, while the Turkish variety was reported by the Journal of Agricultural and Food Chemistry to have superior antioxidant properties. All types of tarragon are good sources of antioxidant vitamins A and C, and excellent sources of various minerals including calcium and manganese (for healthy bones and teeth), copper (an antioxidant), iron (for transporting oxygen in our blood) and magnesium (for healthy muscles and nerves).

Ingredients:
150g chicken – cooked and shredded
50g fresh tarragon - chopped
1 lemon juice and zest
3 tbsp mayonnaise
A pinch of pepper
A pinch of Himalayan crystal salt

Dressing:
1. Shred the cooked chicken.
2. Combine the chicken, mayo, lemon juice, zest and season with pepper.
3. Serve with lettuce or rye bread.

Nutritional analysis per 151g serving: Calories 289 cals, Fat 11.9g (saturated fat 1.6g), Total Carbs 20.9g (sugar 1.4g, fibre 3.2g), Protein 30.4g

10. The Ultimate Salad Bar

I created the ultimate salad bar one weekend while entertaining friends, many of whom had particular food allergies and dislikes. By offering a luxury salad bar everyone could choose foods that they like.

To create the ultimate salad, all you need to do is choose at least one ingredient from each section – how easy is that!

SALAD

Watercress, lettuce, rocket, lambs lettuce, chard, frisée, spinach.

BASICS

Peppers, broccoli (raw), carrots, tomato, white cabbage, red cabbage, avocado, cauliflower (raw), courgette, cucumber, grapes, shiitake mushrooms, olives, sweetcorn, asparagus, beansprouts, mange tout, celery, beetroot, onion, celeriac, kale, red radish, daikon.

GET ADVENTUROUS

Pineapple, pomegranate, nori seaweed, hijiki seaweed, quinoa (cooked), pearl barley (cooked), soba noodles, edamame, artichokes, chicory, fennel, lotus root, endives.

GARNISH

Pumpkin seeds, sunflower seeds, flaxseeds, sprouted mung beans, chickpeas, kidney beans, cress, boiled egg, hemp seeds, alfalfa, meat protein (beef, lamb, chicken, turkey, duck), fish protein (tuna, salmon, haddock, mackerel, sardines, calamari, mussels, shrimp, crab).

NUTS

Macadamias, pecans, almonds, hazelnuts, pistachios, brazil nuts, pine nuts.

Dressings

1. Olive Oil, Lemon and Balsamic

85ml olive oil

1 lemon juiced and zest

1 crushed clove garlic

20ml balsamic vinegar

Options: Add in red chilli, green chilli, fresh herbs, spices, fruit (pomegranate seeds, mango and avocado), tahini or sun-dried tomatoes.

2. Sweet and Sour Dressing

1 inch ginger – grated

2 sun-dried tomatoes

1 tsp mirin

1 tsp tamari

3 tbsp sesame oil

A pinch of pepper

Whizz everything in a food processor until smooth.

3. Kiwi and Orange Dressing

Mix in food processor 100ml olive oil, 1 crushed garlic clove, 2 kiwi (flesh scooped out), juice and flesh of 1 orange, 20ml balsamic vinegar, pinch of pepper, pinch of Himalayan crystal salt.

4. Ginger Dressing

Whisk together 2 tsp grated ginger, 1 crushed garlic clove, 1 tsp Dijon mustard, juice and zest from half an orange, 100ml ground nut oil.

5. Fresh Herb and Coconut Oil Dressing

Whisk together 100ml olive oil, 2 tbsp coconut oil, a few sprigs of chopped mint, basil and chives, a pinch of pepper and a pinch of Himalayan crystal salt.

NOTE: Salad dressing combinations can be simply made by adding oil (see our infused oils section) and vinegar/acid and a seasoning. Here's a simple formula to begin experimenting with your own salad dressing creation:

60% oil of your choice + 30% acid + 10% other ingredient (seasoning, herbs, fruit)

Infused Oils

Infusing base oils with herbs and spices is a great way to naturally add some extra flavour and nutrients. My kitchen has a few and they are also very decorative!

Base Oils:

Extra virgin olive oil
Rape seed oil
Avocado oil
Flaxseed oil
Ground nut oil
Rice bran oil
Grape seed oil
Sesame oil
Other nut oils like walnut oil, macadamia nut oil, pine nut oil, etc

Vinegars and Acids:

Sherry vinegar
Red wine vinegar
Rice vinegar
Balsamic vinegar
Lemon juice
Lime juice

Fun infused oils to try:

Chilli Oil

5 dried chilli peppers
500ml base oil

Rosemary Oil

1 large sprig of rosemary
500ml base oil

Garlic Olive Oil

5 fresh garlic cloves
500ml base oil

Ginger and Citrus Fruit Olive Oil

1 inch fresh ginger cut into chunks
Zest from 1 orange
Zest from 1 lemon
500ml base oil

Soups

1. Sweet Potato Minestrone Soup

When we lived in Japan, we went to our friend's allotment and picked the biggest sweet potatoes I have ever seen. This recipe was created so I could utilise the colossal amounts of sweet potato we picked that day!

Featured ingredient: sweet potato
The orangey colour of sweet potatoes is due to the presence of beta-carotene – the pigment that also makes carrots so orange. Beta-carotene is in fact a form of vitamin A, which is vital for good vision and an essential disease-fighting antioxidant. One medium-sized sweet potato provides your entire daily requirement for vitamin A and a third of your requirement for vitamin C.

Ingredients:
3 sweet potatoes - chopped
2 red onions - chopped
2 stalks celery - chopped
6 ripe tomatoes - chopped
8 sprigs fresh sage - chopped
2 tsp coconut oil
2 litres yeast-free vegetable stock
50g gluten-free spaghetti – broken into
    2-inch pieces
1 red chilli – deseeded and chopped
100g green beans – chopped
1 tsp pepper
1 tsp turmeric

Method:
1. In a fry pan, heat the coconut oil and fry the red onion and celery until golden. Add the sage and red chilli and cook for 1 minute. Set aside.
2. In a large pan, heat the stock and add the seasonings and fried onion, celery, sage and chilli.
3. Add all the chopped ingredients and bring to the boil, then simmer for 25 minutes.

Nutritional analysis per 412g serving: Calories 244 cals, Fat 3.5g (saturated fat 2.4g), Total Carbs 50.6g (sugar 9.2g, fibre 10.1g), Protein 5.2g

2. Lentil and Orange Soup

I love lentils and often throw a small handful into stews, soups and casseroles. I find them filling, tasty and comforting.

Featured ingredient: lentils

Lentils, a small but nutritionally mighty member of the legume family, are a very good source of protein that – unlike animal proteins – don't give us doses of fat at the same time. They are, therefore, an excellent ingredient for people battling illness such as cancer, heart disease, diabetes and obesity. Moreover, lectins - the protein found in lentils – have been found (for example in research at Illinois University) to cause cytotoxicity, which means it may be able to halt cancer growth. Besides being the best provider of protein of any plant, lentils are also a source of vitamin B1 (for a healthy heart and nervous system) and folate (especially required by mums-to-be), and minerals including iron (for oxygen transportation), potassium (for the healthy functioning of nerves and muscles) and molybdenum (a crucial partner for many of our enzymes).

Ingredients:
100g red lentils
2 tsp coconut oil
2 litres yeast-free stock
1 large white onion - chopped
4 stalks of celery - chopped
4 carrots - chopped
1 orange (juice and zest)
1 tsp paprika
1 tsp ground cumin
1 tsp ground coriander
½ bunch fresh coriander

Method:
1. Fry the onion and celery in the coconut oil and set aside.
2. In a small saucepan boil the lentils in water until tender (10 minutes), then skim off the scum, drain and set aside.
3. In a large saucepan, bring the stock to a boil and add the sweet potato, carrots, orange juice and zest, fried onion and celery, spices.
4. Stir occasionally for 15 minutes then add the cooked lentils.
5. Finally, stir in the chopped fresh coriander as a garnish when serving.

Nutritional analysis per 390g serving: Calories 181 cals, Fat 2.9g (saturated fat 2g), Total Carbs 29.7g (sugar 8.6g, fibre 11.3g), Protein 8g

3. Barley Broth (vegetarian)

Another firm favourite for my clients; remove the barley if gluten-intolerant and replace with quinoa or lentils.

Featured ingredient: barley
Barley and other whole grains are good sources of phytonutrients called lignans. The healthy bacteria in our gut converts these into other compounds including enterolactone, which – according to a Danish study on over 800 postmenopausal women - may offer protection against breast and other hormone-driven cancers. Barley is also a good source of fibre and the antioxidant mineral selenium.

Ingredients:
100g pearl barley
100g green split peas
1 small swede – chopped (approx. 300g)
4 carrots - chopped
1 leek - chopped
100g kale – chopped
2 tsp olive oil
2 litres yeast-free stock
Fresh sage – chopped
Fresh rosemary - chopped
A pinch of pepper
A pinch of Himalayan crystal salt
Fresh parsley - chopped
Optional: 200g diced lamb

Method:
1. Soak the green split peas overnight in water.
2. In a large pan heat the olive oil and gently fry the leek until golden then add the swede, carrots, kale.
3. Add the lamb at this time if desired.
4. Add the stock and bring to the boil.
5. Rinse and drain the green split peas and add to the stock.
6. Add the pearl barley, seasoning and herbs.
7. Simmer for 30 minutes stirring occasionally.
8. Serve with fresh chopped parsley.

Nutritional analysis per 311g serving: Calories 261 cals, Fat 3.1g (saturated fat 0g), Total Carbs 47g (sugar 7.3g, fibre 13g), Protein 10.4g

If you added 200g of lamb to this dish:
Nutritional analysis per 361g serving: Calories 354 cals, Fat 6.7g (saturated fat 1.8g), Total Carbs 47.5g (sugar 7.3g, fibre 13g), Protein 24.4g

4. Chunky Vegetable

I'm a big fan of soup and can whip one up with the most unusual ingredients. If you've got any spare vegetables going out of date, then have a go at making a big batch yourself!

Featured ingredient: celery
Celery is certainly useful at helping people lose weight, but it deserves way more credit than that! Surprisingly to some, celery is an excellent source of disease-fighting antioxidants, providing us with a variety of phytonutrients, including vitamin A, vitamin C, flavonoids, phytosterols and phenolic acids. Celery is also believed to lower blood pressure and it's a very good source of vitamin K – necessary for the process of blood clotting. A word of warning around celery is that it is one of a small group of foods that can cause severe anaphylactic shock, so do let guests know if you use it in your cooking!

Ingredients:
2 red onions - chopped
2 tsp olive oil
2 stalks celery - chopped
1 pak choi - chopped
1 clove garlic - crushed
2 litres yeast-free vegetable stock
6 sun-dried tomatoes - chopped
100g borlotti beans - rinsed and drained
100g broad beans - frozen
50g peas - frozen
100g spinach
A few sprigs fresh thyme - chopped
A few sprigs fresh rosemary - chopped
A few sprigs fresh sage - chopped

Method:
1. Heat the olive oil and fry the red onion, celery and garlic.
2. Add the pak choi and sun-dried tomatoes.
3. Add the stock and bring to the boil.
4. Add the beans, peas and fresh herbs and simmer for 25 minutes.
5. In the final moments, add the spinach and take off the heat.

Nutritional analysis per 492g serving: Calories 215 cals, Fat 3.5g (saturated fat 0g), Total Carbs 33.6g (sugar 7.5g, fibre 10.6g), Protein 12.2g

5. Creamy Broccoli Soup

There's loads of great research out about the anti-cancer properties of the awesome superfood, broccoli. We have broccoli at least 2-3 times a week at our house. This soup can be eaten hot or cold.

Featured ingredient: broccoli
Arguably the most healthful food on the planet, this green or purple member of the brassica family is an absolute powerhouse of disease-fighting, free-radical-busting phytonutrients. As well as providing us with generous amounts of vitamins A, C and E, broccoli also provides us with indoles, sulforaphane, thiocyanates, beta-carotene, lutein, zea-xanthin and selenium. Broccoli contains the bioactive compound indole 3 carbinol. It is essential to anyone with hormone problems because it helps denatures oestrogen and even modifies oestrogen receptor sites on cells. It is a powerful epigenetic compound.

Ingredients:
2 heads of broccoli - chopped
2 red onions - chopped
100g potato - chopped
100g watercress - chopped
1 ½ litres yeast-free vegetable stock
100ml rice milk
A pinch of pepper
50g fresh parsley - chopped for garnish

Method:
1. Heat the oil and fry the onions in a large saucepan.
2. Add the stock and bring to the boil.
3. Add the broccoli, potato, pepper and boil for 15 minutes.
4. Bring off the heat and stir in the watercress and rice milk.
5. Blend until smooth.
6. Garnish with chopped parsley.

Nutritional analysis per 251g serving: Calories 84 cals, Fat 0.7g (saturated fat 0g), Total Carbs 16g (sugar 3.5g, fibre 3.6g), Protein 3.5g

6. Borsche

I was first introduced to borsche by my Russian friend, Marina, who lived in the same apartment complex as us in Japan. We would often trade recipes and have cooking parties with Japanese friends, introducing them to some "Western" dishes.

Featured ingredient: beetroot
The characteristic crimson red appearance of beetroot is caused by the presence of betalain pigments such as betanin and betacyanin. There is, in fact, a variety of beetroot coloured by a yellow pigment called beta-xanthin. These betalain pigments are all closely related to the indoles, a family of disease-fighting phytonutrients. Beetroot also provides us with generous quantities of vitamin C and various B vitamins including folate (for making DNA), B3 (niacin, for deriving energy from our food), B5 (pantothenic acid, helps make cell membranes) and B6 (pyridoxine, involved in making insulin, antibodies and neurotransmitters). The green tops of beetroot shouldn't be overlooked as they're a bonus dose of flavonoid antioxidants and vitamin A.

The colourant responsible for the red, purple and blue hues are anthocyanins. These powerful flavonoids have anti-inflammatory properties, they can activate detoxifying enzymes and prevent cancer cell proliferation.

Ingredients:
2 white onions - sliced thinly
2 cloves garlic - crushed
3 tsp coconut oil
2 apples - peeled and chopped
5 beetroots - raw or cooked (vacuum packed)
2 litres yeast-free vegetable stock
A pinch of pepper
Small bunch flat leaf parsley - chopped

Nutritional analysis per 413g serving:
Calories 172 cals, Fat 3.8g (saturated fat 3.1g), Total Carbs 29.7g (sugar 20.6g, fibre 5.9g), Protein 3.2g

Method:
1. In a large saucepan, heat the oil and fry the onion until golden and crispy.
2. Remove half the crispy onion for garnish.
3. Add the beetroot and apple to the remaining fried onion.
4. Stir in the stock and pepper and bring to the boil.
5. Simmer for 15 minutes – longer if using raw beetroot.
6. Remove from heat and blend until smooth.
7. Garnish with crispy onion and flat leaf parsley.

7. Broad Bean Soup

Packed with protein and so versatile, this nourishing soup is easy to make and easy to digest. You can jazz it up by topping it with crispy fried red onions and chicken slivers.

Featured ingredient: broad beans
Broad beans (fava beans) are an excellent, low-fat, plant source of protein, which we need for growth and repair of our body tissues. In terms of reducing our risk of cancer, broad beans are a very good source of fibre, which helps by 'sweeping' toxins out of the colon, and they're rich in phytonutrients called isoflavones. Broad beans also provide us with various B-vitamins, including B1 (thiamin, for deriving energy from food), B6 (pyridoxine, involved in making insulin, antibodies and neurotransmitters) and folate (that essential nutrient for early expectant mothers). Finally, these oft-avoided nutritional powerhouses are an excellent source of several minerals including copper (an antioxidant), iron (for carrying oxygen in the blood) and manganese and phosphorus (both needed for healthy teeth and bones).

Ingredients:
250g broad beans - frozen
1 clove garlic - crushed
1 white onion – chopped
3 tsp olive oil
A pinch of pepper
1 litre yeast-free vegetable stock
A pinch of ground cumin
A pinch of paprika
A few sprigs of fresh sage - chopped
A few sprigs of fresh mint – chopped
A few sprigs of parsley – chop for the garnish

Method:
1. In a large pan heat the oil and fry the onion and garlic.
2. Add the stock and seasoning and bring to the boil.
3. Add the broad beans and fresh herbs.
4. Boil until beans are tender.
5. Remove from heat and blend until smooth.
6. Garnish with a sprinkle of paprika and chopped parsley.

Nutritional analysis per 413g serving: Calories 172 cals, Fat 3.8g (saturated fat 3.1g), Total Carbs 29.7g (sugar 20.6g, fibre 5.9g), Protein 3.2g

8. Sweet Potato and Coconut Soup

This simple yet zesty soup hits the spot every time. You can have it either chunky style or smooth, depending on your preference.

Featured ingredient: coriander
Coriander (cilantro) leaves are a source of several cancer-fighting antioxidant phytonutrients including flavonoids such as quercetin, kaempferol and epigenin, as well as antioxidant vitamins A and C. The leaves are also an excellent source of vitamin K, which is essential for blood clotting and is used in the treatment of Alzheimer's disease. As for minerals, coriander leaves provide us with manganese, which is a co-factor for an antioxidant enzyme called superoxide dismutase.

Ingredients:
4 sweet potatoes - peeled and chopped
250g spinach
4 carrots - chopped
2 red onions - chopped
2 tins coconut milk
1 bunch fresh coriander - chopped
A pinch of pepper
500ml yeast-free vegetable stock

Method:
1. In a large sauce pan, heat the oil and fry the onions until golden.
2. Add the stock and bring to the boil.
3. Add the sweet potato and carrots.
4. Simmer for 15 minutes until vegetables are soft, then add the coconut milk.
5. Take off the heat and blend until smooth.
6. While the soup is still warm, stir in the spinach.
7. Add the chopped coriander and serve.

Nutritional analysis per 219g serving: Calories 93 cals, Fat 2.8g (saturated fat 2g), Total Carbs 11.2g (sugar 2.7g, fibre 3.3g), Protein 4.5g

9. Watercress Soup

I love gardening on the weekends and this soup can be made in a matter of minutes. It is filling and hardy enough to fuel my afternoon of pulling weeds, especially if you throw in a handful of lentils.

Featured ingredient: watercress
Watercress gets its lovely, distinct peppery taste from one of its constituent chemicals, gluconasturtiin, which is converted into a cancer-fighting isothiocyanate. Watercress also contains a compound called 3,3-diindolylmethane (or DIM for short), which has been shown - by research at Georgetown University – that it may provide some protection against the harmful effects of radiatiotherapy. And that's not the end of the story, for watercress provides us with antioxidant vitamins A and C, and antioxidant flavonoids beta-carotene, lutein and zea-xanthin. Finally, of all the vitamins and minerals that watercress supplies us, the most abundant is vitamin K, which is important in the healing of wounds and is being used to treat Alzheimer's.

Ingredients:
300g watercress - chopped
100g peas - frozen
100g potato
1 white onion
2 tsp coconut oil
1 clove garlic - crushed
1 tsp turmeric
A pinch of pepper
1 ½ litres yeast-free vegetable stock

Method:
1. In a large pan heat the coconut oil and fry the onion and garlic until golden.
2. Add the stock and bring to the boil.
3. Add the potato, peas, turmeric and pepper and simmer for 15 minutes.
4. Remove from heat and add the watercress.
5. Blend until smooth and serve.

Nutritional analysis per 219g serving: Calories 93 cals, Fat 2.8g (saturated fat 2g), Total Carbs 11.2g (sugar 2.7g, fibre 3.3g), Protein 4.5g

10. Indonesian "Laske" Soup with Rice Noodles and Coconut Milk

There are a number of similarities between the Mediterranean Diet and many Asian diets: a wide variety of vegetables, favouring fish over red meat, and the popularity of nuts, seeds, beans and lentils. My version of this Indonesian dish features another Asian / Mediterranean parallel: the presence of spices.

Featured ingredient: lemongrass
Growing in clumps, with blades like those of a garden lawn, lemongrass has a delightful lemony aroma. This is due to one of its constituent chemicals, called citral (or lemonal), which has strong anti-fungal and anti-microbial properties. As published in PubMed (an American science journal), lemongrass extracts have shown evidence in a scientific laboratory of being able to kill various types of cancer cells.

Ingredients:
3 tsp coconut oil
1 red onion - chopped
1 inch fresh ginger - grated
2 stalks of lemongrass - split in half
1 bunch fresh coriander - chopped
300g rice noodles
2 pak choi - chopped
150g beansprouts
1 tin bamboo shoots
1 tin water chestnuts
5 red radishes - sliced
1 bunch spring onion - chopped
1 pack baby corn - approx. 10, cut in half
1 tin coconut milk
300ml yeast-free vegetable stock

Method:
1. In a large pan heat the coconut oil and fry the onion, spring onion, ginger and lemongrass.
2. Add the stock and bring to the boil.
3. Add the pak choi, bamboo shoots, water chestnuts, baby corn and simmer for 5 minutes.
4. Add the coconut milk.
5. Add the beansprouts, red radishes and rice noodles.
6. Simmer for 5 minutes and then serve.

Nutritional analysis per 496g serving:
Calories 240 cals, Fat 12.7g (saturated fat 10.6g), Total Carbs 27.6g (sugar 6.8g, fibre 6.3g), Protein 7.5g

Dips

Friday night at our house is usually "staying in and relax" night.
So we have a quick and easy dinner and then we sit in front of the TV
with crudités and dips.

1. Hummous

1 basic chickpea hummous with 5 different add-in ideas (beetroot, harissa spices, pea, spinach, courgette)

Featured ingredient: chickpeas (garbanzos)
Chickpeas (garbanzo beans) have a slightly nutty flavour and are a favourite ingredient of vegetarians as they provide a useful amount of protein. They also provide us with disease-fighting phytochemicals called saponins as well as the antioxidant mineral selenium. Chickpeas are also a good source of fibre, which helps reduce our risk of colon cancer by scouring the wall of our bowel, thus discouraging the build-up of harmful toxins.

Ingredients:
Basic Hummous
1 tin chickpeas (approx. 150g)
2 tbsp tahini
1 lemon (juice and zest)
A pinch of of turmeric
1 clove garlic - crushed
2 tbsp olive oil

Method:
1. Drain and rinse chickpeas.
2. Place all ingredients into food processor and whizz until smooth.
3. Add any add-ins and blend until smooth.

Nutritional analysis per 107g serving: Calories 165 cals, Fat 11.9g (saturated fat 1.7g), Total Carbs 13.5g (sugar 0g, fibre 3.8g), Protein 4.4g

Add-Ins:

1. Lemon and coriander – juice and zest of 1 lemon and half bunch coriander, chopped.

2. Beetroot and parsley – 1 beetroot (cooked and grated) and half a bunch parsley – chopped.

3. Red pepper and paprika – 1 red pepper whizzed in food processor with 1 tsp paprika.

4. Red onion and sage – fry 1 red onion with 5 sprigs of sage and fold into hummous.

5. Kale and pine nut – blanch 50g kale and blend in food processor with 30g pine nuts. You might need to add a touch of water or olive oil.

Extra Add-Ins:

1. Good quality oils – add 1tbsp of any of the following oils: flaxseed, avocado oil, black cumin seed oil, sesame oil, borage oil, starflower oil, coconut oil or extra virgin olive oil.

2. Barley grass powder – blend 10g powdered barley grass.

3. Red chilli or cayenne pepper – finely chop 1 deseeded red chilli or add half tsp cayenne pepper.

4. Nori seaweed – cut 1 nori sheet into small pieces and blend into the hummous.

5. Ground sunflower, pumpkin, flaxseeds and sesame seeds – Add 1 tbsp of seeds and grind in food processor before adding them to hummous.

6. Olives – add 20g of either black or green olives. Whizz in food processor first, before folding into hummous.

7. Avocado – mash one avocado into the hummous.

8. Sun-dried tomato – chop 3-6 sun-dried tomatoes then add to hummous.

9. Cashews – soak cashews in water for a few hours or overnight. Drain and then blend in food processor then fold into hummous.

10. Edamame (soya beans) – blend 50g of edamame until smooth then fold into hummous.

2. Baba Ganoush – Aubergine Dip

Featured ingredient: tahini

Tahini is a thick paste made from ground sesame seeds, which are amazingly mineral-rich and provide us with very useful levels of calcium, manganese and phosphorus (for healthy teeth and bones), iron (for transporting oxygen in our blood), magnesium (for healthy nerves and muscles) and antioxidant minerals copper and selenium. Your muscles will love it – tahini is 20% pure protein, so it's a great post-workout snack when you need to retain muscle strength. Sesame seeds also provide us with a number of useful disease-busting antioxidants, such as sesamol and sesaminol.

Ingredients:
2 aubergines
2 tbsp tahini
1 lemon juice and zest
A pinch of ground cumin
A pinch of paprika
A pinch of pepper
A pinch of Himalayan crystal salt
1 tbsp olive oil

Method:
1. Prick the aubergines with a fork and place them on a pre-heated grill. Turn them occasionally until the skin blisters.
2. Take off heat and peel off skin and discard.
3. Place aubergine in food processor with rest of the ingredients and blend until smooth.

Nutritional analysis per 286g serving: Calories 144 cals, Fat 8.1g (saturated fat 1.1g), Total Carbs 17.8g (sugar 7.3g, fibre 10.4g), Protein 4g

3. Black Bean and Olive

Featured ingredient: black olives

I'm often asked about the difference between black and green olives. Green olives are picked before they're ripe, while black olives are generally picked at peak ripeness. Olives are a staple of a healthy Mediterranean diet, featuring in many salads, while their oil is of course the favoured one for cooking. Olives provide us with a variety of cancer-fighting antioxidant compounds, including oleuropein and oleocanthal – the latter having anti-inflammatory effects akin to ibuprofen. Olive oil also provides us with both omega-6 and omega-3 fatty acids (for a healthy cardiovascular system) in a healthy ratio of 8 to 1.

Ingredients:
100g tinned black beans
50g pitted black olives
¼ red onion - grated
1 clove garlic - crushed
1tbsp apple cider vinegar
½ tsp turmeric
½ bunch fresh coriander - chopped
A few sprigs fresh oregano - chopped
A pinch of pepper

A pinch of Himalayan crystal salt
1 tbsp olive oil
1 red chilli (optional)

Method:
1. Drain and rinse black beans and add to food processor.
2. Add the rest of the ingredients and blend until smooth.
3. Add a touch of water if too thick.

Nutritional analysis per 65g serving: Calories 141 cals, Fat 5.3g (Saturated fat 0.8g), Total Carbs 18.4g (sugar 0.9g, fibre 4.7g), Protein 6g

4. Guacamole

Featured ingredient: avocado

This popular Mediterranean fruit (technically-speaking) is a source of several disease-fighting polyphenolic flavonoid antioxidants such as lutein, beta-carotene and zea-xanthin. As with all antioxidants, they play a vital part in neutralising harmful chemicals called 'free radicals', which are being produced inside us each and every day. Avocados are very good for the heart as they're a good source of monounsaturated fatty acids, such as oleic, palmitoleic and linoleic (omega-6) acids, all of which help to lower bad cholesterol and raise good cholesterol levels.

Ingredients:
1 ripe avocado - mashed
4 tomatoes - chopped
1 red onion - diced thinly or grated
1 lime juice and zest
1 bunch coriander - chopped
A pinch of pepper
A pinch of Himalayan crystal salt

A pinch of turmeric
A pinch of paprika
Optional – 1 red chilli chopped finely

Method:
1. Mix all ingredients together to make a smooth style dip.

Nutritional analysis per 221g serving: Calories 139 cals, Fat 10.2g (saturated fat 2.1g), Total Carbs 13.2g (sugar 5.3g, fibre 6.2g), Protein 2.6g

---

5. Salmon and Dill

Featured ingredient: salmon

Salmon is a good source of the mineral selenium, which plays an important part in the healthy functioning of the thyroid gland and in fighting cancer. This oily fish is also a great source of omega-3 fats, which – as well as being good for the heart - have been linked with a decreased incidence in the lymph and blood cell cancers including leukaemia and non-Hodgkins lymphoma. Salmon is also an excellent source of vitamin B12 (required for a healthy nervous system) and vitamin D (needed for healthy bones, teeth and cartilage). Finally, a word of caution about salmon is that the quality of the water of farmed salmon is not always as clean as it should be, so try to source the wild fish if you can.

Ingredients:
200g cooked smoked salmon, roughly chopped
1 lemon juice and zest
1 spring onion - thinly sliced
½ tsp cayenne pepper
A pinch of pepper

Small handful fresh parsley - chopped
Few sprigs fresh dill - chopped

Method:
1. Combine all ingredients in a food processor and blend until smooth.

Nutritional analysis per 90g serving: Calories 69 cals, Fat 2.4g (saturated fat 0.5g), Total Carbs 2.4g (sugar 0.7g, fibre 1.1g), Protein 9.8g

Herbs and Garnishes

These are all easy to grow in any garden or on any window sill.
I hope you'll be inspired to add a few more garnishes
when you see how brilliant they are for you!
My kitchen, front path and back garden are filled with them!

1. **Rosemary** – scientists have linked this herb's high level of the compound 1,8-cineole to faster and more accurate brain function.

2. **Sage** – sage is full of antioxidants that lower fatty deposits in your arteries and cut bad cholesterol.

3. **Coriander** – a study in the British Journal of Nutrition found that coriander stimulates insulin secretion and balances blood sugar levels.

4. **Oregano** – contains an ingredient called beta-caryophyllene which works as an anti-inflammatory. Oregano is also a powerful yeast and microbe killer.

5. **Thyme** – packed with vitamin K – 1 sprig meets over half your RDA of vitamin K, 10% of manganese and 5% of calcium.

6. **Parsley** – In recent cancer prevention studies parsley was found to be rich in apigenin which reduces the risk of developing cancerous tumours.

7. **Mint** – a potent diuretic that helps flush out excess fluid in the body.

8. **Basil** – at a study in Xinjiang University, it was found that an extract in basil helped reduce blood pressure with similar effects to mild beta blockers.

9. **Chives** – part of the allium family which are renowned for being beneficial to the stomach and colon due to them being rich in organosulfur compounds.

10. **Tarragon** – through history tarragon has been used to numb the mouth and help toothache. The pain-relieving compound contains high levels of eugenol. Also fantastic for helping the production of bile by the liver.

11. **Dill** – is a well-known calmative and can help prevent excess intestinal gas.

Sandwich Toppings
(or serve with a side salad)

Lunchtime can be a bit rushed,
so if you want to fuel your afternoon for maximum energy then
don't skip any meals or cut yourself short on a balanced meal.

1. Coronation Chicken

Featured ingredient: apricots

Apricots are a good source of disease-fighting antioxidants, including vitamins A and C, and polyphenolic compounds such as lutein, zea-xanthin and beta-cryptoxanthin. They are also a source of fibre, which helps to reduce the risk of cancer of the colon. A quick word about apricot pips (kernels). They contain a compound called amygdalin, the natural form of which is sometimes known as vitamin B17. While chewing two or three of these marzipan-tasting seeds may be of small benefit to one's health, there is certainly no evidence that any number of apricot kernels can "cure" any kinds of cancer.

Ingredients:
100g cooked chicken - shredded
1 tsp curry powder
A pinch of pepper
10g dried apricots - chopped
1 tbsp mayonnaise
Optional: chopped chives or parsley

Method:
1. Mix the mayonnaise and curry powder and optional chopped herbs.
2. Fold in the apricots and chicken.
3. Season with pepper.

Nutritional analysis per 32g serving: Calories 55 cals, Fat 2.1g (saturated fat 0g), Total Carbs 1.5g (sugar 0g, fibre 0g), Protein 7.4g

2. Salmon Mousse

Featured ingredient: horseradish

Known for their hot, strong, pungent taste, horseradish, and its more powerful Japanese cousin, wasabi, are two of my favourite condiments. While wasabi is normally found adding some 'oomph' to sushi, horseradish root can be grated on a salad or used as the basis of a dip for dipping raw vegetable sticks (eg carrot, celery, pepper) or to complement a roast dinner. Like other members of the brassica family including cabbage, mustard and kale (Latin name: armoracia), a natural armor is provided by horseradish in the form of antioxidants such as vitamin C and various isothiocyanate compounds.

Ingredients:
100g smoked salmon - chopped
1 tbsp horseradish (make sure the store-bought has no unnecessary ingredients)
1 ripe avocado - mashed
A pinch of pepper
1 lemon juice and zest

Method:
1. Combine all ingredients together.

Nutritional analysis per 94g serving: Calories 137 cals, Fat 11g (saturated fat 2.3g), Total Carbs 6.3g (sugar 0.6g, fibre 4.2g), Protein 5.7g

3. Shrimp, Crayfish and Lemon

Featured ingredient: crayfish

Crayfish, like most seafood, is a very good provider of high quality protein, which is easily digestible and rich in essential amino acids – the ones that our bodies can't make, so we have to get them from the food we eat. Seafood is also a good source of omega-3 essential fatty acids, with crayfish being a particularly good provider of eicosapentaenoic acid (EPA) and docosahexaenoic acid (DHA), which are both important for healthy cell membranes and the healthy functioning of the brain, eyes, kidneys and adrenal glands. Crayfish is also a source of various minerals including calcium (for healthy bones and teeth), iodine (for normal metabolism and growth), zinc (for producing DNA and making testosterone) and selenium (an antioxidant that helps to protect us from illness).

Ingredients:
100g crayfish
50g shrimp
1 red pepper - chopped finely
2 sun-dried tomatoes - chopped
3 tbsp mayonnaise
A pinch of pepper
A pinch of Himalayan crystal salt

Method:
1. Combine all ingredients together.
2. Squeeze ½ lemon over.

Nutritional analysis per 79g serving: Calories 91 cals, Fat 4.3g (saturated fat 0.7g), Total Carbs 5.2g (sugar 2.3g, fibre 0.7g), Protein 7.8g

4. Shiitake Mushroom Pâté

Featured ingredient: shiitake mushrooms

I first became acquainted with shiitake mushrooms in the Chinese restaurants of Sydney, but it wasn't until I lived in Japan that I really began to appreciate them. Growing on a *shii* tree, these *take* (mushrooms) have been widely studied for their immune-boosting and disease-fighting potential. At the heart of these studies have been their polysaccharides, particularly one called lentinan, which has been approved as an anti-cancer drug in Japan. Shiitake mushrooms are also a very good source of

copper (necessary for the formation of red blood cells and a healthy nervous system), selenium (an antioxidant mineral) and vitamin B5 (which helps us derive energy from our food). You can substitute shiitake mushrooms for some wonderful Mediterranean mushrooms like Girolles, Cèpes, Morilles, Bolet, Chanterelles, Pied de Mouton and (I saved the best for last) the beloved Truffle.

Ingredients:
150g shiitake mushrooms
1 onion - chopped
A pinch of pepper
A pinch of Himalayan crystal salt
Small handful parsley - chopped
Few sprigs rosemary - chopped
2 tsp olive oil

Method:
1. Heat the oil in a pan and fry onion and shiitake mushrooms until golden.
2. Season with pepper, salt and herbs.
3. Let cool then whizz in food processor until smooth.

Nutritional analysis per 68g serving: Calories 51 cals, Fat 2.4g (saturated fat 0g), Total Carbs 7.8g (sugar 2.5g, fibre 1.4g), Protein 0.9g

Sushi Slice

If you haven't learned the fine art of rolling sushi, then try my sushi 'sandwich' – where seaweed takes the place of bread. My Japanese friends would be appalled at this lazy way to make sushi, but it is so easy, delicious and fun to do.

Featured ingredient: nori seaweed

Best known in the west for being the wrapping around sushi, nori seaweed is used in a variety of ways in Japan (where nori actually means 'seaweed'). One of my favourite snacks in Japan was onigiri, essentially a ball of rice with a bean or salmon filling, all of which was wrapped in a layer of nori. Seaweed is highly nutritious, providing us with antioxidant vitamins A and C, which, as well as boosting our immune system, are essential for healthy skin and good vision (vitamin A), and healthy bones and blood vessels (vitamin C). Seaweed also provides us with omega-3 fatty acids (for a healthy heart) and a range of minerals, including manganese and calcium (both essential for healthy bones) and iron (required for carrying oxygen in our blood).

Brittany is famous for its nutritious seaweed; shame they don't make sushi sheets.

Ingredients:
250g sushi rice
350ml water
1 pack sushi nori seaweed
Black or white sesame seeds
1 tsp wasabi paste
1 ripe avocado - mashed
1 cucumber - sliced with grater to make long thin strips
200g smoked salmon or you can use tinned salmon or tuna
1 lemon - cut into wedges to squeeze on sushi bite.

Nutritional analysis per 134g serving:
Calories 152 cals, Fat 3.9g (saturated fat 0.6g), Total Carbs 23.4g (sugar 0.6g, fibre 2g), Protein 6.2g

Method:
1. Place the rice in a bowl and run cold water over it to gently wash it. Repeat 2-3 times until water runs clear.
2. Bring 350ml of water to the boil then add rice and simmer for 10 minutes.
3. Turn off heat and let stand for 15 minutes.
4. Place a nori sheet shiny side down.
5. Spread a thin layer of rice on the nori sheet with a wet wooden spoon.
6. Mash avocado with the wasabi paste and place a thin layer over the rice.
7. Place the long strips of cucumber over the avocado spread then place the salmon on top.
8. Squeeze lemon on top of the salmon and then top with black sesame seeds.
9. Cut into bite-size squares.

DINNER

> ## *"A man seldom thinks with more earnestness of anything than he does of his dinner."*
> Samuel Johnson

Round the day off with a main meal designed to introduce the whole spectrum of colours to your table.

Whether you love meat, prefer fish or simply enjoy vegetarian food we've included something here for everyone.

NOTE: where your budget allows, please choose grass-fed organic meat where possible.

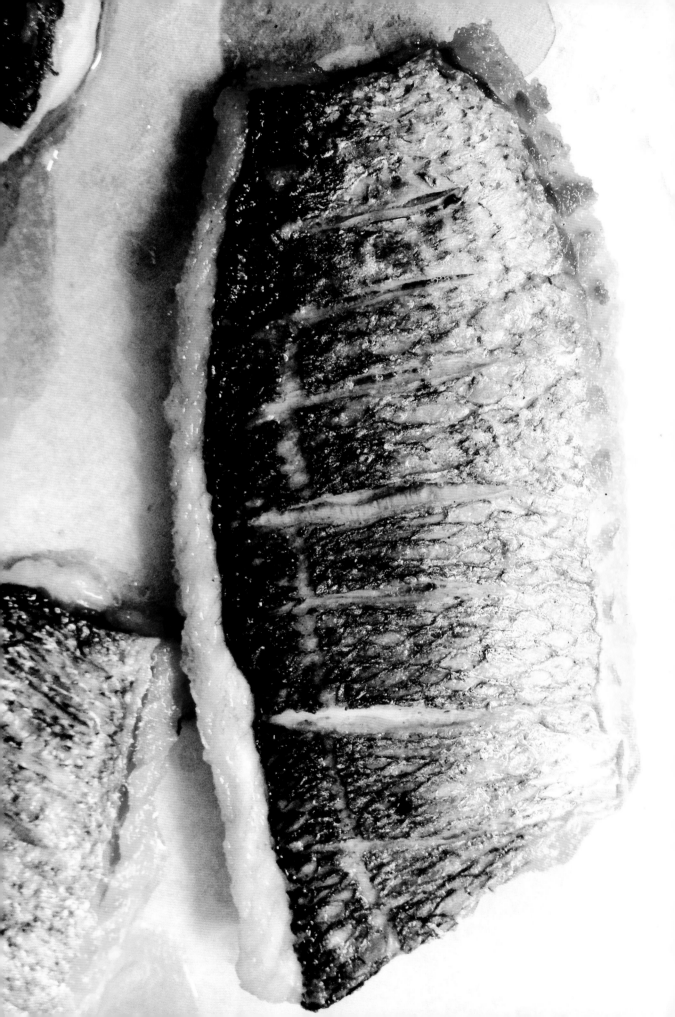

1. Chicken Bites
with Coconut Topping

I first made these for one of my body building clients looking for different ways to have chicken. He now makes them in large batches and freezes them, so that he always has a good quality protein snack available after the gym.

Featured ingredient: chicken
Chicken is a great source of protein - a 100g portion providing around a third of the protein we need every day for healthy cell structure, repair and maintenance. It's a 'lean' meat, meaning it doesn't contain much fat, which is why it's often the meat of choice for the health-conscious, including people who do a lot of sport. Chicken also provides us with vitamin B3 (niacin, essential for a healthy nervous system, manufacturing DNA and converting our food into energy).

Ingredients:
500g ground chicken
1 egg - whisked
1 red onion - finely chopped
1 clove garlic - crushed
1 small handful fresh parsley - chopped
1 tsp turmeric
1 inch fresh ginger - grated
100g finely ground almonds
50g unsweetened shredded coconut
A pinch of pepper
A pinch of Himalayan crystal salt

Nutritional analysis per 206g serving:
Calories 510 cals, Fat 31.3g (saturated fat 11.2g), Total Carbs 12.5g (sugar 4g, fibre 6.1g), Protein 44.4g

Method:
1. Pre-heat the oven to 180°C.
2. In a bowl combine the shredded coconut and only 50g finely ground almonds.
3. In a separate bowl combine the ground chicken, 50g finely ground almonds, onion, garlic, ginger, turmeric, pepper and salt. Mix well until everything is combined.
4. Roll the mixture into about 20 balls and roll in the shredded coconut and finely ground almond mixture.
5. Bake on an oven tray with greaseproof paper at 180°C for 20-25 minutes until juices run clear and the coconut is golden toasted.

2. Duck with Cinnamon, Star Anise and Orange

"And what happens if you don't like duck?" was the question asked of hotel owner Basil Fawlty in the classic comedy Fawlty Towers. With charming awkwardness Basil responded, "If you don't like duck, you're rather stuck!" I'm pleased to say that if you don't like duck then there are plenty of other recipes to choose from in this section!

Featured ingredient: duck

Duck meat provides us with similar levels of protein as chicken, but it's a source of more vitamin B2 (riboflavin, needed for deriving energy from our food) and more iron (an essential component of haemoglobin, which plays a vital role in transporting oxygen to all parts of our body).

Ingredients:
For the glaze:
1 tsp coriander seeds
1 tsp fennel seeds
75ml tamari
2 oranges (juice and zest)
1 inch fresh ginger - grated
½ tsp cinnamon
A pinch of turmeric
A pinch of pepper
4 star anise
4 bay leaves
1 tbsp honey
1 red chilli – chopped finely (optional)

Duck:
4 duck breasts (at least 85g each breast)

Method:
1. Prepare the duck and remove the skin, then gently score the duck breast to allow the glaze to seep in.
2. Make the glaze by combining all ingredients and placing in a pan.
3. Boil the ingredients until it thickens, then set aside.
4. Gently fry the duck until sealed on all sides, then pour the glaze over the duck and simmer for 10 minutes.
5. If the glaze dries out it will burn, so add a touch of water if needed.

Nutritional analysis per 316g serving:
Calories 312 cals, Fat 7.1g(saturated fat 0.1g), Total Carbs 19.6g (sugar 13g, fibre 3.5g), Protein 39.1g

3. Chicken with a Walnut Topping

This has been one of my favourite recipes for years, so I hope you like it too!

Featured ingredient: walnuts

Perfect for building into a dinner, sprinkling on top of a salad or eating loose as a snack, walnuts are a superb source of energy, nutrients and colon-cleansing fibre. They're a good source of omega-3 fatty acids, which help our cardiovascular system by raising levels of good cholesterol and lowering levels of bad cholesterol. This helps by reducing strain on our heart and blood vessels, making it less likely that we'll suffer a heart attack or a stroke. Walnuts are also a good source of disease-busting phytochemicals (or 'fighto-chemicals' as I think of them), including melatonin, carotenoids, ellagic acid and vitamin E. Walnuts contain lots of minerals, too, for example manganese (for healthy bones), copper (for healthy nerves and a healthy heart) and magnesium (for healthy muscles).

Ingredients:
For the walnut topping:
75g walnuts - chopped finely
1 clove garlic - crushed
1 inch fresh ginger - grated
A pinch of pepper
3 tsp olive oil
4 chicken breasts

Method:
1. Pre-heat the oven to 180°C.
2. Combine all the ingredients for the walnut topping and make into a paste. You may need to add a touch more oil.
3. Evenly split the topping mixture into 4 and press onto the top of each chicken breast.
4. Place chicken breast on baking sheet and bake in oven for 20-30 minutes, until juices run clear.

Nutritional analysis per 172g serving: Calories 426 cals, Fat 25.4g (saturated fat 4.1g), Total Carbs 2.5g (sugar 0g, fibre 1.3g), Protein 46.8g

4. Chicken with Thai-Style Butternut Squash and Roasted Cashews

This recipe is just full of flavour and packed with nutritional benefits. The roasted cashews add that perfect crunch. It can be a perfect vegetarian dish too, just by removing the chicken!

Featured ingredient: butternut squash
Butternut squash – a member of the pumpkin family – is amazingly healthful, providing us with a useful amount of carbohydrate energy, a wide range of minerals, and astonishingly high levels of vitamin A (100g of butternut squash provides over three times our recommended daily allowance). As well as being a useful antioxidant, this vitamin is vital for healthy skin and mucous membranes, healthy bones and good vision (especially at night). Butternut squash seeds make a great snack, especially when roasted, as they're a good source of protein (for growth and repair), potassium (for healthy nerves and muscles), and the essential amino acid tryptophan.

Ingredients:
4 skinless chicken breasts
1 small butternut squash (approx. 400g)
2 tsp coconut oil
1 red onion – sliced
1 bunch spring onions – chopped finely
30g cashews
2 inch fresh ginger – grated
1 lemongrass stalk – sliced lengthways in half
1 clove garlic
1 lime juice and zest
200g sugar snap peas
Small handful fresh coriander – chopped
2 tins coconut milk
1 red chilli - optional

Method:
1. Heat the coconut oil in a wok and fry the red onion and spring onion.
2. Add the diced chicken, ginger, lemongrass and garlic and stir-fry until chicken is golden.
3. Add the cashews and optional red chilli.
4. Add the butternut squash and lime juice and zest.
5. Add the coconut milk.
6. Simmer for 15 minutes, then add the sugar snap peas and simmer for a further 10 minutes.
7. Take off the heat, add the coriander, then stir.

Nutritional analysis per 382g serving: Calories 402 cals, Fat 16.9g (saturated fat 5.7g), Total Carbs 14.9g (sugar 5.7g, fibre 3.3g), Protein 46.2g

5. Turkey
Tikka Burger

These little burgers are bursting with goodness and are so quick and easy to make. Adjust the tikka spice to taste and serve with a fresh salad, rice or vegetables.

Featured ingredient: turkey

Turkey is nutritionally very similar to chicken. Both are excellent sources of protein, providing us with the full range of amino acids that we need for growth and repair of our body tissues. A couple of subtle differences are that turkey is saltier than chicken (as turkey meat contains more sodium), but turkey contains less saturated fat than chicken.

Ingredients:

500g lean turkey mince

1 red onion – chopped thinly

30g sweetcorn

1 tbsp tikka spice paste

20g black sesame seeds

1 small bunch fresh coriander - chopped

4 tbsp coconut oil

Method:

1. Combine the turkey mince, onion, sweetcorn and tikka paste until thoroughly mixed.
2. Evenly split into 6 burgers and roll in black sesame seeds before flattening out into patties.
3. Heat coconut oil in fry pan and fry burgers until golden on both sides and cooked thoroughly in the centre.

Nutritional analysis per 227g serving: Calories 387 cals, Fat 26.8g (saturated fat 12.5g), Total Carbs 9.4g (sugar 4.8g, fibre 2.7g), Protein 27.3g

Fish Dishes

1. Moroccan Spiced Fishcakes *(Haddock)*

In 2009 I trekked 102 miles in the Sahara Desert for charity and was fortunate to eat the most amazing food in Marrakesh before and after the trek. I spent loads of time talking to spice stall holders about the famous Moroccan blend of Ras el Hanout, which literally means "head of the shop" and can have up to 40 different spices included in the blend depending on the stall holder! It is generally composed of black pepper, cardamom, mace, nutmeg, long pepper, clove, turmeric, ginger, galangal, cubeb, cinnamon, sedge, iris, lavender, baharat, nigella and monk's pepper.

Featured ingredient: haddock
Haddock is a very good source of protein, which we need for growth, repair of body tissues and for giving structure to our cells. Haddock is also a source of omega-3 and omega-6 essential fatty acids (important for the health of our cardiovascular system), although not in such useful quantities as oily fish like salmon, mackerel, trout, tuna and sardines. Haddock is a good source of various vitamins including niacin (which helps us derive energy from our food), vitamin B6 (plays a role in making insulin) and vitamin B12 (for a healthy nervous system). Haddock is also a good source of phosphorus (for healthy bones and teeth) and selenium, an antioxidant mineral that plays an important role in combating illness.

Ingredients:
800g haddock fillets
600g potatoes – peeled and chopped
1 lemon (juice and zest)
4 tsp capers
2 tbsp Ras el Hanout spice mix
1 inch fresh ginger – grated
Small bunch of coriander - chopped
1 egg
Paprika to dust over

Nutritional analysis per 394g serving:
Calories 264 cals, Fat 4g (saturated fat 0.7g), Total Carbs 3.9g (sugar 0g, fibre 0.8g), Protein 50.3g

Method:
1. Boil the potatoes, drain and mash.
2. Poach the haddock, drain and crumble apart.
3. In a bowl, combine all ingredients and mix thoroughly.
4. Form into even balls and flatten into patties.
5. Pre-heat oven to 180°C.
6. Place on a baking tray with greaseproof paper. Dust with paprika.
7. Bake in the oven for 20-25 minutes, until golden.

2. Mediterranean Sea Bass

Served with seasonal fresh vegetables, this meal is simple, healthy and utterly delicious!

Featured ingredient: sea bass
Sea bass is nutritionally similar to haddock (described above). They both provide us with almost identical levels of protein and the bone-strengthening mineral phosphorus. However, sea bass is a much better source of omega-3 essential fatty acids eicosapentaenoic acid (EPA) and docosahexaenoic acid (DHA), meaning

that sea bass would be a more preferable ingredient for people concerned about cardiovascular issues such as blood pressure and cholesterol levels. Sea bass is also a source of more of the mineral selenium, which, by being a component of glutathione enzymes, plays an important role in neutralising harmful, cancer-causing free radicals.

Ingredients:
4 sea bass fillets
2 tsp olive oil
1 red onion - diced
1 yellow pepper - diced
1 red pepper - diced
1 tsp fresh oregano
1 tsp fresh thyme
1 tsp fresh rosemary
A pinch of pepper
A pinch of Himalayan crystal salt

Method:
1. Heat the olive oil and fry the onion and peppers.
2. Add the fresh herbs, tamari and seasoning.
3. Add the sea bass fillets and cover pan to help cook thoroughly.

Nutritional analysis per 220g serving: Calories 156 cals, Fat 3.7g (saturated fat 0.6g), Total Carbs 7.9g (sugar 2.4g, fibre 2g), Protein 24.1g

3. Salmon in a Watercress Sauce

I once went to a watercress fayre and was blown away by all the stalls serving watercress in such fun and interesting ways. This watercress sauce can be poured over poultry, meat, vegetables, pasta and even replace the hollandaise sauce for eggs.

Featured ingredient: Himalayan crystal salt
Formed by the evaporation of ancient seas millions of years ago in the now mountainous region that's home to Mount Everest, the jagged pink crystals of Himalayan crystal salt are a beauty to behold – especially if you've got a magnifying glass to hand! It provides us with a wide variety of trace minerals and adds a delicate flavour to meals.

Ingredients:
4 fillets of salmon
For the watercress sauce:
1 white onion - chopped
1 small bunch of chives - to garnish
150g watercress
100ml yeast-free vegetable stock
2 tsp coconut oil
A pinch of white pepper
A pinch of Himalayan sea salt

Method: For the watercress sauce:
1. Fry the onion in 2 tsp coconut oil.
2. Add the 100ml stock and bring to boil.
3. Take off the heat then add the watercress, stir until wilted.
4. Add seasoning to taste.
5. Whizz with hand blender until the sauce is smooth.
Poach the salmon in a touch of water until cooked through. Serve salmon and pour over sauce and garnish with chives.

Nutritional analysis per 238g serving: Calories 310 cals, Fat 14.5g (saturated fat 5g), Total Carbs 2.7g (sugar 1.3g, fibre 1.1g), Protein 42.4g

4. Chilli Mussels

I adore mussels and, luckily, so does my family! They're quick, easy, nutritious, fun and never any leftovers – except the sleepy ones that don't open up, you shouldn't eat these as they won't be thoroughly cooked.

Featured ingredient: mussels
Mussels are an excellent source of two vital minerals: manganese (essential for a healthy nervous system) and selenium (a disease-fighting antioxidant), as well as being a good source of iron (for carrying oxygen in our blood) and phosphorus (for healthy teeth and bones). Mussels are also an excellent source of vitamin B12, which is necessary for making DNA (the substance that makes our genes), for making red blood cells and for the healthy functioning of our nervous system. They're a good provider of essential fatty acids as well (for a healthy cardiovascular system), crucially supplying a greater concentration of omega-3 than omega-6 molecules.

Ingredients:
1.5 kg fresh mussels – beards removed!
1 red onion - sliced
4 spring onions - chopped
1 red chilli – sliced
3 tbsp tamari
1 inch fresh ginger – grated
1 clove of garlic
2 tbsp olive oil

Nutritional analysis per 307g serving:
Calories 457 cals, Fat 6.7g (saturated fat 3.9g), Total Carbs 87g (sugar 1.7g, fibre 3.2g), Protein 10.9g

Method:
1. Prepare the mussels – remove beards and rinse.
2. Heat the olive oil in a pan and fry red onion, garlic, chilli and ginger.
3. Add the tamari.
4. Add the mussels.
5. Add a touch of water if needed.
6. Occasionally shake the pan until all the mussels open and cook thoroughly.
7. Remove from pan; discard any mussels that haven't opened.
8. Sprinkle the spring onion over the mussels and serve.

5. Kedgeree

Such an easy mid-week dinner to whip up, and leftovers make a superb breakfast or lunch the following day, too! Add 200g of your favourite fish to step 3 if desired.

Featured ingredient: turmeric

This root vegetable (related to ginger) has a distinct orange colour due to a powerful antioxidant pigment called curcumin, which studies have indicated may have anti-tumour and anti-inflammatory effects. Turmeric is very high in vitamin B6 (pyridoxine), which plays an important part in manufacturing insulin and histamine, and very high in iron (for carrying oxygen in our red blood cells) and manganese (for a healthy nervous system).

Ingredients: For the rice:
400g brown basmati rice
1 tbsp turmeric
500ml water
For the kedgeree base:
1 tbsp coconut oil
1 red onion - chopped
1 clove garlic - crushed
A pinch of turmeric
5 strands saffron
1 bunch spring onion - chopped
1 lemon (juice and zest)
2 hard-boiled eggs
2 stalks celery
½ bunch fresh parsley
A pinch of pepper
A pinch of Himalayan sea salt

Method: For the rice:
1. Rinse the rice until water runs clear.
2. Bring 500ml water to boil and add the turmeric.
3. Add the rice, then simmer for 10-15 minutes until soft.

For the kedgeree:
1. Boil 2 eggs in water until hard-boiled.
2. Fry the onion, spring onion, garlic and celery in the coconut oil.
3. Add the seasoning, turmeric, saffron, pepper and salt.
4. Turn off the heat and fold in the cooked rice.
5. Grate the lemon zest and juice the lemon, then add to rice mixture.
6. Add the chopped parsley.
7. Top with boiled egg halves.

Nutritional analysis per 307g serving: Calories 457 cals, Fat 6.7g (saturated fat 3.9g), Total Carbs 87g (sugar 1.7g, fibre 3.2g), Protein 10.9g

Meat Dishes

1. Lamb Tagine

When I visited Marrakesh my friend and I ate at this tiny restaurant specialising in tagine dishes. Wow – what a culinary delight that was! I often create tagines during the winter months, as the spices are so warming and uplifting.

Featured ingredient: lamb

Lamb is a good source of protein, although the meat does contain saturated fat. It provides us with useful amounts of vitamin B12 (needed for a healthy nervous system and making DNA), and niacin and riboflavin (both necessary for extracting energy from food). Lamb is also a source of various minerals including zinc (required by the immune system and in making testosterone), phosphorus (for healthy bones and teeth) and iron (for oxygen transportation).

Ingredients:

1 kg diced lamb
2 red onions – thinly sliced
2 cloves garlic – crushed
1 inch fresh ginger - grated
1 tsp ground ginger
2 tsp ground cumin
2 tsp coconut oil
2 tbsp Ras el Hanout spice
200g chopped tomatoes - tinned
150ml yeast-free vegetable stock
20g dried apricots - chopped
20g dried prunes - chopped
½ bunch fresh coriander - chopped
½ bunch fresh parsley - chopped
1 pomegranate – all seeds used for garnish

Method:

1. Fry the diced lamb, onion, garlic and ginger in the coconut oil.
2. Add the chopped tomatoes.
3. Add the stock and then the ground ginger, cumin, Ras el Hanout.
4. Add the dried fruit and bring it all to the boil.
5. Simmer for 1 – 2 hours until lamb is incredibly tender. You might need to add more stock water so it doesn't simmer dry in the pan.
6. Take off heat and stir in coriander and parsley.
7. After serving – garnish with pomegranate seeds.

Nutritional analysis per 413g serving: Calories 566 cals, Fat 21.1g (saturated fat 8.6g), Total Carbs 19g (sugar 12.6g, fibre 2.8g), Protein 72.1g

2. Venison Bhuna

Game meats are very naturally flavoursome and when joined with spices, the flavour and nutritional content are both intensified!

Featured ingredient: venison

If you want to savour a red meat with fewer calories and less fat than lamb or beef, then venison is your best choice. Just like lamb, it's a good source of protein, B vitamins and minerals, especially zinc (required by the immune system and in making testosterone), phosphorus (for healthy bones and teeth) and iron (for oxygen transportation). Game meats are part of the Rainbow Diet as they have more omega-3 than mass market meats. Travel inland 30 minutes from the French coast and game is on the menu!

Ingredients:
1 kg venison - diced
2 inches fresh ginger - grated
2 cloves garlic - crushed
1 fresh red chilli - minced
3 large tomatoes - chopped
3 red onions - chopped
1 tsp turmeric
2 tsp ground cumin
2 tsp ground coriander
1 bunch fresh coriander
2 tsp coconut oil
150ml water

Method:
1. Fry the onion, garlic, fresh ginger, chilli and diced venison until venison is browned.
2. Add the chopped tomatoes.
3. Add the turmeric, ground cumin, ground coriander and water.
4. Bring to the boil and simmer until venison is cooked thoroughly.
5. You might need to add more water so the pan doesn't simmer dry.
6. When venison is tender, stir in chopped fresh coriander.

Nutritional analysis per 397g serving: Calories 334 cals, Fat 5.1g (saturated fat 2g), Total Carbs 9.7g (sugar 3.1g, fibre 2g), Protein 56.4g

3. Lamb Chilli

During my teens in Ottawa, Canada, lamb chilli was a dish that my mum made when I brought friends home after a day skating on the Ottawa Canal. Warm, comforting, nutritious, packed with flavour and packed with memories!

Featured ingredient: tomatoes
The beautiful red colour of tomatoes is due to the presence of lycopene – a carotenoid, disease-fighting antioxidant pigment which, interestingly, appears to be more concentrated or bioavailable in cooked tomatoes and purées. Tomatoes also provide us with good levels of various vitamins, especially vitamin A (for healthy eyes, skin and mucous membranes) and vitamin C (a powerful, immune-boosting antioxidant).

Ingredients:
500g lamb mince
2 tsp coconut oil
1 red onion - chopped
2 cloves garlic - crushed
2 carrots - chopped finely
3 stalks celery - chopped finely
1 red pepper - diced
1 tsp ground cumin
1 tsp ground coriander
1 tsp cayenne pepper
1 tsp Worcester sauce
250g tinned chopped tomatoes
2 tbsp tomato paste
100g kidney beans (tinned)
A pinch of pepper
A pinch of Himalayan crystal salt
½ bunch fresh coriander - chopped

Method:
1. Fry the onion, garlic, celery until golden.
2. Add the lamb mince and fry until lamb is browned.
3. Add the chopped tomatoes and tomato paste, followed by the ground cumin, coriander, cayenne pepper, Worcester sauce, pepper and salt.
4. Add the pepper and carrots and simmer for 10 minutes.
5. Add the kidney beans and simmer for a further 10 minutes.
6. To garnish – sprinkle with chopped fresh coriander.

Nutritional analysis per 359g serving: Calories 397cals, Fat 10.8g (saturated fat 5g), Total Carbs 28.3g (sugar 7.3g, fibre 7.3g), Protein 45.8g

4. Lamb Burgers

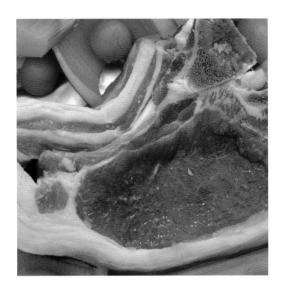

When it comes to eating burgers, Barbara's burgers are the best burgers! Make them in a larger batch as they're perfect for freezing. Serve with seasonal vegetables.

Featured ingredient: red onions
Red onions (Spanish onions) have a similar nutritional profile to their more widely used white relative; one of the few differences being that red onions contain less allyl propyl disulphide – an antioxidant that gives onions their distinctive pungent smell. Onions also contain useful amounts of immune-boosting vitamin C, as well as the flavonoid quercetin - an antioxidant that seems to play a part in fighting cancer and heart disease.

Ingredients:
500g lamb - minced
1 red onion –finely chopped
1 handful fresh parsley – chopped
1 handful fresh coriander – chopped
1 egg – beaten
A pinch of pepper
A pinch of Himalayan crystal salt
1 tsp whole grain mustard
30g sesame seeds to roll the burgers in

Method:
1. Preheat the oven to 180°C.
2. In a bowl combine the minced lamb, chopped onion, parsley, coriander, pepper, salt, mustard, then add the egg and mix thoroughly.
3. Split the mixture into 8 patties and roll into a ball.
4. Roll the lamb balls in the sesame seeds then flatten into patties.
5. Place on a baking sheet then in the oven for 20-25 minutes until juices run clear.

Nutritional analysis per 182g serving: Calories 306cals, Fat 14.7g (saturated fat 4.4g), Total Carbs 4.1g (sugar 1.9g, fibre 2.1g), Protein 38.4g

5. Meatball Curry (Lamb or Venison)

When I was young, my father used to have his cricket friends around for a game of cards a few times a year. One of his West Indian friends always used to bring this meatball curry, and it was fabulous!

Featured ingredient: garlic
If garlic didn't have such a pungent odour, I'm sure that a lot more people would benefit from its phenomenal health benefits. Garlic contains about five times more vitamin C than onion, ten times more immune-boosting vitamin B6, and fifteen times more of the mineral manganese, which we need for healthy bones. Garlic also contains a group of substances which convert into allicin (needed for a healthy heart and blood vessels) when the clove is cut or crushed.

Ingredients:
500g minced lamb or venison
1 clove garlic
2 white onions – chopped
1 tsp garam masala spice
1 egg
2 tsp coconut oil
1 tsp cumin seeds
1 inch fresh ginger – grated
400g tomatoes – chopped
1 tbsp tomato puree
1 tsp turmeric
Water – if necessary

Method:
For the meatballs:
1. Preheat oven to 180°C
2. Mix the minced lamb, 1 chopped onion, garam masala and egg until fully combined.
3. Form into about 24 small balls.
4. Bake in oven until golden – approx. 15-20 minutes.

For the curry:
1. In a pan fry the left over onion, cumin seeds, fresh ginger.
2. Add the tomatoes and tomato puree.
3. Add the turmeric and a touch of water if needed.
4. Add the cooked meatballs and simmer for 10 minutes.

Nutritional analysis per 295g serving: Calories 306cals, Fat 12.2g (saturated fat 5.3g), Total Carbs 7.8g (sugar 1.8g, fibre 2.0g), Protein 41.2g

Vegetarian

I'm a massive advocate of food variety and there is no doubt
that some vegetarian dishes offer a greater variety of ingredients than
your meat and two veg dishes. So for non-vegetarians, try some of these dishes
and remember, variety is, quite literally, the spice of life!

1. Falafels

Featured ingredient: mung beans
Mung beans contain a group of phytonutrients called phenols - powerful antioxidants
that appear to show encouraging signs of fighting cancer in research studies. Mung beans
are a good source of folate – a B vitamin that plays a vital role in making DNA for new
cells, and is especially important for a mother to consume in early pregnancy. Mung
beans are also a source of protein and a range of minerals including manganese (for
healthy bones), magnesium (for healthy bones, nerves and muscle) and phosphorus (also
vital for our bones). As you can see, bones are dependent on a lot more nutrients than
calcium!

Ingredients:
100g sprouted or tinned chickpeas
100g sprouted or soaked and boiled
mung beans
1 egg
1 onion – grated
50g chickpea flour
A sprinkle of water if needed

Different spices to add:
Moroccan spiced falafel: Raz al Hanouh
and fresh coriander
Italian spiced falafel: lemon zest and
oregano
Thai spiced falafel: lemongrass, ginger,
red chilli
Chinese spiced falafel: Chinese 5-spice

Method:
1. Blend the chickpeas, mung beans and
   onion in a food processor.
2. In a bowl combine the bean mix with
   chickpea flour and the egg.
3. Add different spices according to
   taste.
4. Preheat oven to 180°C or deep-fry the
   falafel in rapeseed oil until golden
   brown.

Nutritional analysis per 101g serving:
*Calories 250cals, Fat 4g (saturated fat
0.6g), Total Carbs 39.6g (sugar 5.9g,
fibre 11.4g), Protein 15.1g*

2. Caribbean Spiced Bean Burgers

One of my favourite places on the planet is Barbados and I love the seasonings they use there. These spicy bean burgers were served at a beach hut selling local food and they certainly hit the spot after hours of snorkelling!

Featured ingredient: adzuki beans
You've probably guessed by their name that these beans are especially popular in Japan. There they are deployed in numerous ways, famously in a sweetened red bean paste as a result of the creation of Anpanman – an animated cartoon character whose name literally means 'adzuki bean bread man'! However, I'm sorry to tell you Anpanman, I much prefer adzuki beans when used more healthily in savoury situations! I'm impressed by the protein levels of adzuki beans, and I'm especially impressed by the wide variety of minerals and the levels of folate (essential for making DNA) and thiamin (needed to convert food into energy).

Ingredients:
400g adzuki beans – tinned
1 red onion - chopped
1 red pepper – diced small
1 lemon (juice and zest)
1 egg
Small bunch fresh parsley - chopped
Small bunch fresh chives - chopped
1 tsp ground paprika
2 inches fresh ginger - grated
Few sprigs fresh thyme
1 tsp Caribbean Allspice or jerk
    seasoning
3 tbsp coconut oil – to fry

Method:
1. In a food processor blend the adzuki beans, onion and pepper.
2. Move mixture to a bowl and add the lemon juice, lemon zest, all fresh herbs and spices. Mix well.
3. Add the whisked egg to help combine.
4. Split into 12 burgers and shallow fry until golden on each side.

Nutritional analysis per 186g serving:
Calories 271cals, Fat 12.2g (saturated fat 9.4g), Total Carbs 28g (sugar 2.8g, fibre 7.7g), Protein 11.7g

3. Brazil Nut Burgers

I created these burgers for a client who is a vegetarian athlete. I needed something tasty, high in protein, filling and easy to make.

Featured ingredient: Brazil nuts

A staple food of tribes of the Amazon for thousands of years, these nutritional powerhouses grow in some of the tallest trees, many of which are over 500 years old. They're high in energy and protein and supply us with an absolutely dazzling array of nutrients. Let's start with minerals. Brazil nuts are an amazing source of the free-radical-fighting antioxidants selenium and copper, an excellent source of phosphorus and magnesium (both needed for healthy teeth and bones), and a good source of manganese (for a healthy nervous system), zinc (for making DNA) and iron (for oxygen transportation). Their supply of vitamins is nearly as generous, for they provide us with vitamin B1 (thiamin, for a healthy nervous system) and vitamin E (an antioxidant that's vital in the body's constant battle to neutralise cancer-causing 'free radicals'). Finally, Brazil nuts are good for the heart as they're a great source of healthy fatty acids, such as palmitoleic and oleic acid, both of which help to lower levels of bad cholesterol and raise levels of good cholesterol.

Ingredients:
500g cooked quinoa
4 stalks of celery - finely chopped
3 carrots - grated
1 onion - chopped finely
Small bunch parsley - chopped
250g Brazil nuts - chopped finely
100g flaxseeds
5 tsp tamari
A pinch of pepper
50ml olive oil
1 egg

Method:
1. Cook 500g quinoa in 500ml water until fluffy, then set aside. Add more water if necessary.
2. Grind the Brazil nuts and flaxseeds until they are finely chopped.
3. Combine cooked quinoa, Brazil nuts, flaxseeds, carrots, onion, celery, parsley, tamari and pepper.
4. Add the egg to combine then split the mixture into 12 small patties.
5. Shallow fry in the olive oil or bake in the oven at 180°C for 20-25 minutes.

Nutritional analysis per 223g serving: Calories 781cals, Fat 47.2g (saturated fat 9.4g), Total Carbs 69g (sugar 2.8g, fibre 14.7g), Protein 22.8g

4. Sweet Potato Polenta with Asian Vegetable Fricassée

I've always enjoyed the versatility and velvety texture of polenta, yet not many people use it. If you have any leftover sweet potato polenta mix, then line a muffin tray, pour the mix in and freeze. These little rounds of polenta are great topped with a fried egg for a quick lunch!

Featured ingredient: polenta

This Italian dish, which is more popular in some parts of the country than pasta, is usually made from corn, although it can be made from other grains. Depending on which brand you buy, it can be a useful source of minerals, including manganese, magnesium and phosphorus, all of which are essential for healthy bones.

Ingredients:

450ml yeast-free vegetable stock

1 large sweet potato - diced

600ml coconut milk

175g quick-cook polenta

2 tbsp coconut oil

1 clove garlic - crushed

2 cm fresh ginger - grated

500g shiitake mushrooms - sliced

1 courgette - use a potato peeler to make ribbons

100g sugar snap peas

1 red onion - sliced

1 small head of broccoli - cut into florets

2 carrots - peeled, then use a potato peeler to make ribbons

Nutritional analysis per 345g serving:
Calories 632cals, Fat 28.9g (saturated fat 25.4g), Total Carbs 100g (sugar 7.9g, fibre 7.6g), Protein 6.7g

Method: To make the polenta:

1. Place the stock and sweet potato together and boil for 15 minutes.
2. Remove from heat and hand-blend until smooth.
3. Return to the pan and add the coconut milk.
4. Add the polenta and stir constantly for 5-7 minutes until you achieve the desired consistency.

To make the fricassee:

1. Heat the coconut oil. Fry the garlic, red onion and ginger for 1 minute.
2. Add the mushrooms and fry until golden.
3. Add the broccoli and a touch of water.
4. Add the courgette and carrot ribbons.
5. Add the sugar snap peas.
6. To serve, evenly portion the polenta at the bottom of a bowl and place the vegetable fricassee on top.

5. Watercress Potato Cakes with a Red Radish Salsa

My watercress and potato cakes are a perfect starter, side dish or as a main with seasonal vegetables.

Featured ingredient: red radish
Radishes are a good source of vitamin C (ascorbic acid) - the most important vitamin for boosting immunity, while also being vital for the formation of collagen (a protein necessary for strengthening our bones, skin, hair and blood vessels). Radishes are a good source of various disease-fighting phytonutrients including indoles, isothiocyanates and flavonoids; in fact, the red pigment in red radishes is due to the presence of a particular type of flavonoid called anthocyanins.

Ingredients:
150g watercress - chopped
200g potatoes - diced
1 small bunch chives - chopped
1 egg whisked
A pinch of paprika
A pinch of cumin
A pinch of pepper
A pinch of Himalayan crystal salt
For the radish salsa:
8 red radishes - sliced thinly
1 tomato - chopped
Few sprigs coriander - chopped
1 red chilli - chopped (optional)
A pinch of pepper

Method:
For the watercress potato cakes:
1. Boil the potatoes until soft, then drain and set aside.
2. Preheat oven to 180°C.
3. In a bowl, mash the potato and add the chopped watercress, chives and seasoning. Add the egg and fully combine.
4. Split evenly and make into 8 patties.
5. Place on a baking tray and bake for 20-25minutes.
For the red radish salsa:
1. Combine all ingredients and serve with watercress potato cakes.

Nutritional analysis per 100g serving watercress cakes: Calories 59cals, Fat 1.4g (saturated fat 0g), Total Carbs 8.2g (sugar 0.8g, fibre 1.7g), Protein 3.3g

Nutritional analysis per 200g serving Salsa: Calories 10cals, Fat 0.1g (saturated fat 0g), Total Carbs 1.8g (sugar 0.8g, fibre 0g), Protein 0.4g

6. Risotto

Risotto was one of my favourites in my skating years - I loved my carbs with big flavour. These days I like to add more vegetables, meats, fish and green tea (ochagohan) to my risotto.

Featured ingredient: rice
We all know that brown rice is healthier than white rice, which is why I'm surprised that the normally health-conscious Japanese favour Mount Fuji-summit-coloured brilliant white grains over the duller brown ones. White rice actually starts off brown, but then it gets refined – a process that removes its bran and its germ, and, with it, many of its nutrients. Brown rice is a good source of B vitamins, including B1 (thiamin, for a healthy heart and nervous system), B3 (niacin, for deriving energy from food), B5 (pantothenic acid, for making cell membranes) and B6 (pyridoxine, for making insulin). It's also a good source of various minerals, including manganese, magnesium and phosphorus, all of which are essential for healthy bones.

Basic Risotto – this basic risotto is nutritious and great just on its own or you can choose to add extras from the variations below. This recipe is meant to be smooth and not stodgy, so you may need to adjust the stock.

Ingredients:
400g risotto rice (or you can use brown rice, red rice, add a few grains of wild rice or even use quinoa)
1 litre yeast-free vegetable stock
2 tbsp olive oil
1 clove garlic
½ head of celery
1 white onion
½ tsp pepper
½ tsp Himalayan crystal salt

Method:
1. In a frying pan, add the oil, celery, onion and garlic. Fry until golden brown then add the rice and stir until coated with the oil, then set aside.
2. Heat the stock to boil then add the rice mixture and stir.
3. Simmer until rice absorbs stock, stirring every 3-4 minutes.
4. If you want to add in extra ingredients – you can choose from any of the following ideas.

Risotto Ideas:

1. **Beetroot risotto** - Add 2 chopped cooked beetroot, juice and zest of half a lemon and cracked pepper to taste. Add this at Stage 4.
2. **Shiitake and pea** - Slice 100g of shiitake mushrooms and add to stage 1 of the cooking process. Add 50g of frozen peas at stage 4.
3. **Kale, edamame and matcha** - Chop finely 100g of kale and add to stage 1 of the cooking process. Add 50g of frozen edamame (soya beans) and half tsp matcha green tea at stage 4.
4. **Asparagus and fresh herb (basil, parsley, chives)** - Chop 100g of asparagus, 25g each of basil, parsley and chives and add to stage 4 of the cooking process.
5. **Fresh lemon and sage** - Juice and zest 1 lemon and chop 50g of fresh sage and add it to stage 4 of the cooking process.

Nutritional analysis per 225g serving: Calories 443cals, Fat 7.7g (saturated fat 1.2g), Total Carbs 82.9g (sugar 1.3g, fibre 2g), Protein 7.5g

7. Lentil and Spinach Dhal, Served with Grilled Okra and Aubergine

Comforting, warming, tasty and nourishing, you'll love this rainbow recipe!

Featured ingredient: okra

Okra (or "lady's finger") is a plant of North-East African origin, the fruit of which is popular in stews, stir-fries and curries. The fruit contains a slimy substance (not in an off-putting way!) called mucilage, which is known to improve the movement of food through the digestive system, possibly benefiting people suffering from constipation. Okra is an excellent source of several vitamins including vitamin K (essential for blood-clotting), vitamin C (renowned as an immune-booster), vitamin B1 (thiamin, helps extract energy from food) and vitamin B6 (pyridoxine, involved in making insulin, antibodies and neurotransmitters).

Ingredients:
250g red lentils
1.2 litres water
1 red onion - chopped
1 inch fresh ginger - grated
1 fresh green chilli - seeds removed and chopped finely
1 garlic - crushed
1 tsp ground coriander
1 tsp cumin
1 tsp turmeric
250g spinach
A pinch of pepper
A pinch of Himalayan crystal salt
1 tsp sesame oil
100g okra
1 aubergine

Method:
1. Bring the water to a boil, then add the lentils, then simmer.
2. Skim the foam from the lentils, then, when the foam stops appearing, add the ground coriander, cumin and turmeric.
3. After 10 minutes, stir in the onion, ginger, green chilli, garlic and season with pepper and Himalayan crystal salt. Constantly stir the dhal to ensure it doesn't burn. Add more water if needed. Cook until lentils are soft and have absorbed all the water.
4. Remove from the heat. Stir in the spinach as it will wilt quickly.
5. In another pan, fry the okra and aubergines in sesame oil, then set aside to serve with the dhal.

Nutritional analysis per 415g serving: Calories 206cals, Fat 1.7g (saturated fat 0g), Total Carbs 35.8g (sugar 5g, fibre 18g), Protein 13.5g

8. Stuffed Squash with Shiitake Mushrooms and Beans

On the weekends, I prefer to make a dish I can pop into the oven, then either spend some time in the garden or prepare for a busy week ahead in my office at home. This recipe was created just for that!

Featured ingredient: red chilli peppers
They've had an American rock band named after them and they're the focus of eating challenges watched by millions of people on You Tube, but these unassuming-looking little fruit pods deserve to be respected the world over for their important health benefits. 'Capsicum annum', as you'd call them if you spoke Latin, are a member of the nightshade family, meaning they're related to tomatoes, potatoes and aubergines. Red chilli peppers get their distinctive colour from particular antioxidant carotenoids called capsanthin and capsorubin, which, like other antioxidant nutrients, help combat disease such as cancer by neutralising harmful chemical fragments called 'free radicals'. Chilli peppers are also an extremely good source of perhaps the most important of all antioxidants – good old vitamin C!

Ingredients:
1 butternut squash
2 tsp olive oil
1 clove garlic
1 red chilli pepper
1 tsp turmeric
1 inch grated ginger
200g shiitake mushrooms - sliced
100g ready-cooked adzuki beans
100g ready-cooked chickpeas
100g ready-cooked black beans
2 stalks of celery - sliced
Handful of parsley
½ tsp pepper
½ tsp Himalayan crystal salt

Method:
1. Pre-heat the oven to 180°C.
2. Cut the butternut squash in half and scoop out all the seeds.
3. Brush with oil.
4. Place on non-stick baking tray, cover with foil and bake for 30 minutes.
5. In a fry pan, add oil and fry the garlic, celery, shiitake mushrooms, chilli.
6. Add the beans and seasoning.
7. Place bean mixture into the butternut squash and put back into the oven for a further 12-15 minutes until the butternut squash is soft.
8. Garnish with parsley and serve.

Nutritional analysis per 298g serving: Calories 335cals, Fat 3.2g, (saturated fat 0g), Total Carbs 77.2g, (sugar 5.2g, fibre 7.9g), Protein 8.4g

9. Thai Spiced Rice Noodles with Vegetables

When we lived in Japan we often flew home with Thai Airways via Bangkok. There was a restaurant at the airport that would tailor the spice to suit the family ranging from spicy for my husband to mild for the kids! This was always my favourite dish.

Featured ingredient: ginger
This knobbly-looking underground rhizome has been used for centuries by different cultures as a remedy for digestive complaints. This is probably due to its many, amazingly-named essential oils including gingerol, zingerone, shogaol, farnesene, citral, cineol and beta-phelladrene, which are believed to be anti-inflammatory, anti-bacterial, anti-flatulent and analgesic (pain-killing).

Ingredients:
225g rice noodles
2 cloves garlic
2 inches fresh ginger - grated
1 red pepper - sliced
1 stalk celery - chopped
1 red onion - sliced
3 spring onions - chopped
100g beansprouts
1 small bunch fresh coriander - chopped
30g cashews
30g flaked almonds
2 tbsp coconut oil
3 tsp tamari
1 tsp fish sauce (optional)
A pinch of cayenne pepper
A pinch of pepper
1 tin coconut milk

Method:
1. Boil 500ml water and drop in the rice noodles, stir for 3-5 minutes until cooked, then set aside.
2. Heat the coconut oil and fry the onion, celery, garlic, ginger and spring onions.
3. Add the pepper and beansprouts and stir-fry for 1 minute.
4. Add the coconut milk then the tamari, fish sauce, cayenne and pepper.
5. Bring to the boil then add the rice noodles.
6. Remove from heat and garnish with cashews, almonds and coriander.

Nutritional analysis per 309g serving: Calories 291cals, Fat 16.2g (saturated fat 8.6g), Total Carbs 31g (sugar 6.9g, fibre 5g), Protein 7.4g

10. Millet, Carrot and Sesame Burgers

Vegetarian cooking has always been a passion of mine and I always made the vegetarian menu for my clients first, so that they never sensed like they were an afterthought. Yet whenever I make these millet burgers, it's always the carnivores that dive in first!

Featured ingredient: millet

Eating a wide variety of healthy ingredients is essential to good health as it means we will be consuming a wide variety of important nutrients. Millet happens to be a great alternative to other grains in our diet. It's a good source of fibre (essential for 'sweeping' toxins out of the colon) as well as important disease-fighting phytonutrients called lignans. Millet is also a good source of the mineral magnesium, which is vital for the healthy functioning of the muscles and nerves.

Ingredients:

100g cooked millet
750g carrot - grated
400g tinned ready-cooked chickpeas
1 red onion - diced
3 tsp tahini paste
1 tsp cumin
½ tsp pepper
½ tsp paprika
½ tsp Himalayan crystal salt
1 egg
3 tbsp olive oil
1 lemon (juice and zest)
5 tbsp sesame seeds

Method:

1. In a food processor, blend the chickpeas, carrot, onion, tahini, cumin, pepper, paprika and egg into a thick paste consistency.
2. Place mixture into a bowl and fold in the cooked millet and lemon juice and zest.
3. Divide the mixture into 6-8 patties. Roll into burger shape then roll them in the sesame seeds.
4. In a non-stick pan, heat the oil and fry each burger until golden on each side.

Nutritional analysis per 294g serving: Calories 380cals, Fat 20.5g (saturated fat 3.1g), Total Carbs 44g (sugar 11.1g, fibre 9.8g), Protein 8.9g

The Ultimate Pizza

As a working mum, pizza was always the answer when my kids
wanted to bring friends home for dinner.
As you can imagine, I'm not a store-bought pizza lover so the ideas below
have been firmly tested on teens!

The pizza dough can take a couple of hours by hand, but if you have a bread machine
with a pizza dough setting then that really helps.

---

1. Gluten-free pizza base
(makes three 12-inch thin crust bases, so you can cook and freeze unused bases)

Ingredients:
85g brown rice flour
85g tapioca four
7g easy-blend yeast
2 tsp xanthan gum
2 tbsp olive oil
150ml warm water
Optional at this stage: half tsp pepper,
half tsp Himalayan crystal salt, half tsp
herbs like rosemary, thyme, sage,
oregano, tarragon, etc.

Method:
1. Mix all the ingredients together and
   place in a bread machine on a pizza
   dough setting or knead by hand until
   thoroughly combined.

Nutritional analysis per 52g serving:
*Calories 212cals, Fat 7.6g (saturated fat
1.1g), Total Carbs 34g (sugar 0g, fibre
1g), Protein 2.1g*

2. Almond flour pizza base

Ingredients:
325g almond flour
2 tbsp coconut flour
½ tsp baking powder
½ tsp fresh rosemary – chopped
½ tsp fresh sage – chopped
½ tsp Himalayan crystal salt
A pinch of pepper

3 eggs – whisked
2 tbsp olive oil

Method:
1. Pre-heat oven to 180°C.
2. Line a baking tray with greaseproof
   paper.

continued on page 106

2. Almond flour pizza base

Method continued:

3. In a mixing bowl combine almond flour, coconut flour, baking powder, freshly chopped rosemary and sage, salt and pepper.
4. In a separate bowl, whisk the eggs and oil until frothy.
5. Pour the wet ingredients into the dry ingredients and mix together to form dough.
6. Shape the dough into a ball and transfer it onto an oven dish lined with greaseproof paper.
7. Place greaseproof paper on top of the dough and then flatten to desired size and thickness.
8. Bake the crust for 10-15 minutes, until the edges start to crisp and brown.
9. Add the toppings and place back in oven for a further 10-15 minutes until all ingredients are cooked.

Nutritional analysis per 119g serving:
Calories 219cals, Fat 18.9g (saturated fat 3.3g), Total Carbs 7.4g (sugar 1.2g, fibre 3.7g), Protein 8.1g

3. Cauliflower pizza base

Ingredients:
750g cauliflower
1 garlic - crushed
2 eggs - whisked
100g ground almonds
1 tsp fresh rosemary - chopped
1 tsp fresh sage - chopped
A pinch of pepper
A pinch of Himalayan crystal salt

Method:

1. Pre-heat the oven to 180°C.
2. Cut the cauliflower into chunks and pulse in the food processor until finely chopped like the consistency of rice.
3. Place all the "cauliflower rice" into a pan of boiling water for 5 minutes.
4. Drain and pour onto a clean tea towel and squeeze all water out of the cauliflower. Transfer to a clean bowl.
5. Stir in the almonds, crushed garlic, rosemary, sage, pepper and salt.
6. Add the eggs and combine well.
7. Line a 30cm round baking tray with greaseproof paper. Brush with oil.
8. Put the cauliflower mixture on the paper and spread evenly, pressing firmly into the pan.
9. Bake for 15 minutes, until slightly golden.

NOTE: you can replace cauliflower with grated carrot, grated courgette or experiment with your favourite vegetable.

Nutritional analysis per 236g serving:
Calories 225cals, Fat 14.9g (saturated fat 1.7g), Total Carbs 16g (sugar 6g, fibre 8.1g), Protein 12g

4. Pizza bases

A) Tomato base

B) Pesto base

C) Hummous base

D) Olive paste base

E) Sun-dried tomato base

5. Pizza toppings

This is where it gets really fun! For the Rainbow Pizza choose at least 1 topping from each colour of the rainbow.

RED - Adzuki beans, beetroot, kidney beans, pomegranates, radishes, red lentils, red peppers, tomatoes.

ORANGE - Apricots, carrots (TIP: grated carrot looks like cheddar cheese!), ginger, saffron, squash blossoms, swedes, sweet potatoes, turmeric, yams, yuzu (zest).

YELLOW - Apple cider vinegar, artichokes, bamboo shoots, bean sprouts, burdock, cauliflower, celeriac, chestnuts, chickpeas, coconut oil, corn, daikon, eggs, fish (particularly oily fish), garlic, horseradish, lentils, lemons, lotus root, maitake mushrooms, millet, nuts, olive oil, onions, parsnips, pineapples, potatoes, quinoa, raw honey, rutabaga, salsify, seeds, shiitake mushrooms, sprouted beans, star fruit, taro, turnips, yellow peppers.

GREEN - Alfalfa, asparagus, artichokes, avocado, broccoli, cabbage, capers, celery, chard, chives, chicory, courgettes, edamame (soya beans), flaxseeds, fennel, green lentils, green beans, green tea, herbs, kale, kohl rabi, leeks, lemongrass, limes, okra, olives, pak choi, peas, pumpkin seeds, rocket, runner beans, seaweeds, snow peas, spinach, spring onions, sprouted mung beans, sugar snap peas, wakame seaweed, watercress, wasabi, wheatgrass.

BLUE - Black-eyed peas, dulse, hijiki, kombu, laver, nori.

INDIGO - Blackberries, dates, juniper.

VIOLET - Aubergine, beetroot, dates, figs, olives, red onions, shallots.

Side Dishes

1. Wild Rice and Millet

Ingredients:
150g millet
50g wild rice
300ml yeast-free vegetable stock
A pinch of pepper

Method:
1. Bring the stock to the boil.
2. Add the millet and wild rice, then simmer for 20 minutes.
3. Season with pepper.

Nutritional analysis per 50g serving: Calories 186cals, Fat 1.7g (saturated fat 0g), Total Carbs 36g (sugar 0g, fibre 4g), Protein 6g

2. Spring Greens with Chestnuts

Ingredients:
150g chestnuts (vacuum-packed)
250g spring greens (kale, chard, pak choi or green cabbage) - shredded
1 clove garlic- crushed
2 tsp olive oil

Method:
1. Heat the oil and fry the garlic.
2. Add the greens and stir-fry for 5 minutes. Add a touch of water if required.
3. Break up the chestnuts to tiny chunks then add the chestnuts to the mix.

Nutritional analysis per 100g serving: Calories 105cals, Fat 2.8g (saturated fat 0g), Total Carbs 17.5g (sugar 11g, fibre 1.4g), Protein 3g

3. Red Cabbage, Onion and Apple

Ingredients:
150g red cabbage, 1 red onion
1 red apple, 1 tbsp tamari
A pinch of pepper
A pinch of Himalayan crystal salt
A pinch of turmeric, 2 tsp olive oil
1 inch fresh ginger – grated

Method:
1. Heat the oil and stir-fry the onion, cabbage, apple and ginger.
2. Add a touch of water if required.
3. Add the tamari, pepper, salt and turmeric.

Nutritional analysis per 118g serving: Calories 67cals, Fat 2.5g (saturated fat 0g), Total Carbs 11.4g (sugar 7.2g, fibre 2.7g), Protein 1.4g

4. Roasted Tomatoes with Pesto

Ingredients:

6 tomatoes - cut in half

To make your own pesto in a food processor:

1 bunch basil

2 tsp olive oil

1 clove garlic - crushed

1 lemon juice and zest

A pinch of pepper

50g pine nuts (or try almonds, Brazil nuts or hazelnuts)

Method:

To make the pesto:

Put all ingredients into the food processor and whizz until smooth.

You may need to add a touch more oil.

Place a tsp pesto on top of each tomato half and bake in the oven for 15 minutes at 180°C.

Serve with the rest of the pesto.

Nutritional analysis per 31g serving: Calories 109cals, Fat 10.9g (saturated fat 0.9g), Total Carbs 3.5g (sugar 0g, fibre 1.2g), Protein 2g

5. Fennel and Pak Choi with Orange

Ingredients:

1 fennel bulb - shredded

2 pak choi - chopped

1 orange - zest and segments

30g hazelnuts, 2 tsp sesame oil

A pinch of pepper

1 red chilli - chopped finely

Method:

1. Heat the sesame oil and fry the chilli, fennel and pak choi for 5 minutes.

2. Add the orange segments and zest and pepper to taste.

3. Serve with hazelnuts as garnish.

Nutritional analysis per 150g serving: Calories 161cals, Fat 8g (saturated fat 0.8g), Total Carbs 15g (sugar 5g, fibre 6.9g), Protein 8.5g

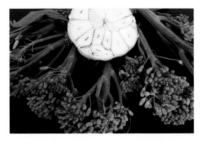

6. Brassicas with Garlic

Ingredients:

1 head of broccoli

1 small head of cauliflower

1 clove garlic - minced

2 tsp tamari

2 tsp chilli-infused olive oil (see section on infused oils)

Method:

1. Boil broccoli and cauliflower until tender.

2. Drain then toss with garlic, tamari and chilli-infused olive oil.

Nutritional analysis per serving of 100g: Calories 52cals, Fat 2.6g (saturated fat 0g), Total Carbs 6.2g (sugar 1.7g, fibre 2.3g), Protein 2.8g

7. Brussels Sprouts with Almonds and Pomegranate Seeds

Ingredients:
250g Brussels sprouts
30g flaked almonds
¼ pomegranate - seeds removed for garnish
1 tsp sesame oil - to drizzle

Method:
1. Boil the Brussels sprouts until tender, then drain.
2. Toss in the flaked almonds, sesame oil and then garnish with pomegranate seeds.

Nutritional analysis per 70g serving: Calories 85cals, Fat 5.6g (saturated fat 0.6g), Total Carbs 6.2g (sugar 1.7g, fibre 2.9g), Protein 4g

8. Sweet Potato and Miso Mash

Ingredients:
400g sweet potato
2 tbsp white miso paste
2 tsp fresh rosemary - chopped

Method:
1. Boil the sweet potato until tender. Drain and mash.
2. Stir in the miso paste and rosemary.

Nutritional analysis per 110g serving: Calories 110cals, Fat 0.8g (saturated fat 0g), Total Carbs 23g (sugar 8g, fibre 4.1g), Protein 3g

9. Chickpea and Ginger Stew

Ingredients:
250g tinned chickpeas - rinsed and drained, 250g chopped tomatoes
1 red onion - chopped
1 clove garlic - chopped
1 inch ginger - grated, 2 tsp tomato paste
A pinch of turmeric, a pinch of pepper

Method:
1. Fry the onion, ginger and garlic in oil.
2. Add the chopped tomatoes, tomato paste and turmeric.
3. Add the chickpeas, season with pepper.
4. Simmer until fully combined and thickened.

Nutritional analysis per157g serving: Calories 79cals, Fat 0.9g (saturated fat 0g), Total Carbs 14.4g (sugar 3.2g, fibre 3.2g), Protein 3.8g

10. Stuffed Pepper

Ingredients: 1 red pepper, 1 yellow and 1 green pepper, all halved and de-seeded
1 clove garlic - crushed
1 small bunch parsley - chopped
1 small bunch basil - chopped
6 caperberries (or plain capers) - chopped
3 anchovies - chopped
3 tomatoes - chopped, 2 tsp olive oil

Method:
1. Pre-heat oven to 180°C.
2. Prepare the peppers on a baking tray and drizzle with oil.
3. Mix the garlic, parsley, basil, anchovies and chopped tomatoes.
4. Put the mixture into the peppers and bake for 15-20 minutes.
5. Garnish with caperberries

Nutritional analysis per 130g serving: Calories 65cals, Fat 1.8g (saturated fat 0g), Total Carbs 7.2g (sugar 0g, fibre 2.1g), Protein 5.8g

DESSERT

"Work is the meat of life, pleasure the dessert.

B.C.Forbes

When working with clients, I generally work on an 80:20 rule - 80% really healthy food and 20% not so healthy. When the body is suffering from a serious illness though, I pull this back to a 90:10 rule. In that 10% some 'treats' are allowed, such as those below.

Special note for gluten-free cooking: Xanthan or Guar Gum is the key to successful gluten-free baking. It provides the binding needed to give the baking product proper elasticity, keeping it from crumbling.

1. Sorbet – one of the most refreshing desserts and bursting with flavour.

My freezer is packed with sorbets! I make them, freeze them in ice cube trays, then store them in zip-lock bags. They are great to add to smoothies, plain water or just a portioned treat when I feel like a tangy flavour burst.

Featured ingredient: mango
Known as "the king of fruits", mangoes have been satisfying people with their delicious juiciness for thousands of years. They were particularly popular in ancient India, where they were important in the Ayurveda system of medicine – where a patient's prescribed path to wellness was based on their "body type". The orange colour of mangoes is due to the presence of phytonutrient flavonoids, such as alpha-carotene and beta-carotene - a form of vitamin A, which helps us to see in the dark and is important for healthy skin and membranes. Mangoes are also an excellent source of immune-boosting vitamin C.

Ingredients: The sorbet base:
110ml water
5 tbsp coconut nectar sugar
500g of chosen fruit base
Add a flavour: Single flavours: (choose 500g of each fruit to add to mix)
Mango, watermelon, apple, orange, pear, lemon, peach, apricot, papaya, fig, cherry, grape, strawberry, blackberry, raspberry, pineapple, melon, kiwi, blueberry, Sharon fruit, dragon fruit
Get adventurous:
Rhubarb and ginger, Pineapple and chilli, Nectarine, pomegranate and mint, Orange and cocoa, Matcha green tea and lemon, Decaf coffee and vanilla bean

Method:
1. In a pan heat the water and melt the coconut nectar sugar, then cool.
2. In food processor blend 500g of chosen fruit or fruit combo – be creative!
3. Combine the water and blended fruit, then transfer to a shallow freezer-proof container.
4. Use a fork to break up the ice crystals every 30 minutes.
5. Cover and freeze for 3 hours until set.

Nutritional analysis per 30g serving of Sorbet Base without the fruit: Calories 38cals, Fat 0g (saturated fat 0g), Total Carbs 10g (sugar 10g, fibre 0g), Protein 0g

Average with 500g fruit added: Nutritional analysis per 150g serving: Calories 144cals, Fat 0.3g (saturated fat 0g), Total Carbs 35g (sugar 30g, fibre 2.2g), Protein 1g

2. Rhubarb with Cinnamon Crumble

My mother-in-law, Audrey, makes the most amazing crumbles and she's learned to adapt her recipe to be wheat-free and dairy-free for our visits! Thanks Audrey, the greatest mother-in-law I could have asked for!

Featured ingredient: rhubarb
According to the history books rhubarb has been grown for its medicinal properties since 2700BC (in China). Since then scientists have determined that rhubarb is a source of several vitamins, such as vitamin C and various B vitamins, but the vitamin in the most significant concentration is vitamin K – which is essential in the process of blood clotting. As for minerals, rhubarb is a source of two elements vital for healthy bones and teeth: calcium and manganese.

Ingredients:
3 tbsp spelt or gluten-free flour
50g coconut palm sugar
2 eggs - whisked
1 orange - zest only
1 inch ginger - grated
1 kg fresh rhubarb - chopped
60g spelt or gluten-free flour
50g coconut palm sugar
120g dairy-free margarine
2 tsp cinnamon
160g porridge oats

Nutritional analysis per 280g serving:
Calories 368cals, Fat 14.2g (saturated fat 3.1g), Total Carbs 54g (sugar 13g, fibre 8g), Protein 7.6g

Method:
1. Pre-heat the oven to 180°C.
2. Mix the 50g coconut sugar, 3 tbsp spelt flour, eggs, orange zest and ginger until well combined.
3. Add the rhubarb and mix thoroughly.
4. Pour the rhubarb mixture into the bottom of an oven-proof dish.
5. In a mixing bowl, combine the 60g spelt flour, coconut sugar, dairy-free margarine and cinnamon. Crumble the mixture with your hands then add the oats.
6. Gently pat the oat mixture on top of the rhubarb mixture.
7. Bake until rhubarb bubbles over – after around 40 minutes.

3. Chocolate and Hazelnut Dairy-Free Ice Cream

I have a love/hate relationship with ice cream as my daughter once suffered food poisoning after she ate one that I bought her at a beach kiosk. If your immune system is low it's best that you avoid this particular treat as it's one of the high risk foods for food poisoning. This is a great recipe and doesn't last long at all in our freezer as it tastes like a frozen Ferrero Rocher chocolate!

Featured ingredient: hazelnuts
Hazelnuts are highly healthful little nuggets of nutrition. They provide us with generous quantities of fibre (that 'sweeps' toxins out of our colon), protein and essential fatty acids (such as linoleic, which is important for the health of our heart and blood vessels). As for vitamins, hazelnuts are an excellent source of vitamin E (which neutralises harmful 'bits of chemicals' called 'free radicals'), vitamin B1 (thiamin - which we need for a healthy heart and nervous system), vitamin B6 (pyridoxine – helps make insulin, antibodies and neurotransmitters) and folate (helps make DNA and is vital in early pregnancy). Hazelnuts give us a plentiful supply of minerals, too, including manganese (for healthy bones), copper (an antioxidant, amongst other roles), iron (for transporting oxygen around our body) and magnesium (for the healthy functioning of nerves and muscles).

Ingredients:
200ml chocolate hazelnut non-dairy milk (or rice milk)
100ml soya cream
60g coconut palm sugar
1 egg yolk
1 avocado
15g 100% cocoa powder
35g hazelnuts - chopped
35g 80% dark chocolate - chopped

Method:
1. Combine the hazelnut milk, soya cream, coconut palm sugar, egg yolk and cocoa powder.
2. In an ice cream maker, add the chocolate mixture and follow the ice cream maker instructions. Add the chopped chocolate and hazelnuts in the last 2 minutes of the process.
3. Transfer to a container and freeze for 3 hours.

Nutritional analysis per 95g serving: Calories 220cals, Fat 16.2g (saturated fat 3.8g), Total Carbs 18g (sugar 9.3g, fibre 4.6g), Protein 3.4g

4. Whole Fruit Popsicles (Ice Lollies)

These are wonderful to have on hand when you need a treat. The combinations are endless and really fun to make.

Featured ingredient: kiwi

These amazing little nutritional gems were first cultivated in China (and are still known as the 'Chinese gooseberry'), but made commercially popular in New Zealand (hence the name 'kiwi fruit'). They're a good source of bowel-healthy fibre, but an amazing source of immune-boosting antioxidant vitamin C, with 100g of the fruit providing over one and a half times our daily requirement. Kiwis are also a very good source of vitamin K, which we need so that our blood clots when we get injured.

Ingredients:
150g fresh fruit (see the list)
100ml water

Fresh Fruit List: apple, mango, kiwi, orange, passion fruit, pineapple, lychee, pear, cranberry, strawberry, banana, blueberry, plum, dragon fruit, lemon, watermelon, melon, grapefruit, peach, nectarine, blackberry, pomegranate, star fruit, papaya, cantaloupe and fig.

Nutritional analysis per 63g serving of Kiwi Ice Lolly: Calories 23cals, Fat 0.2g (saturated fat 0g), Total Carbs 5.5g (sugar 1.1g, fibre 3.4g), Protein 0.4g

Method:
1. Blend ingredients together.
2. Pour the mixes into clean ice lolly moulds and freeze for 3 hours.
3. You can layer the ice lolly with different fruit mixes. Freeze half the mould with one flavour. Two hours later, add the top layer and continue to freeze for another two hours until solid.
4. You can also make it a fruit salad style with whole pieces of fruit. Pour the smooth mix in then add whole pieces of fruit and freeze for 2-3 hours.
5. You can also have a smooth-blended style.

5. Roasted Plums, Nectarines and Pineapple with Rose Water

Our plum tree provides us with a great yearly crop, so I often make this super healthy dessert and just pop it in the oven. For an extra crunch, you can sprinkle chopped nuts or seeds over this dessert.

Featured ingredient: plums

Delicious, juicy Prunus domestica are a source of a variety of disease-fighting antioxidants. The rich red colour of the fruit is due to one of these - an anthocyanin, whose pigment is also responsible for the beautiful hues of various berries, including raspberries, strawberries and blackberries. Other antioxidants provided by prunes include the flavonoids lutein and zea-xanthin, and vitamins A and C.

Ingredients:

6 plums - cut in half and pit taken out

4 nectarines - cut in half and pit taken out

¼ pineapple - cut into slices

3 tsp coconut palm sugar

1 pomegranate - scrape seeds out

2 tsp rosewater

Method:

1. Preheat oven to 180°C.
2. Arrange the fruit on a baking tray and sprinkle the coconut palm sugar and add rosewater.
3. Bake for 20-25 minutes, until fruit is soft.
4. Garnish with pomegranate seeds.

Nutritional analysis per 170g serving: Calories 114cals, Fat 1.1g (saturated fat 0g), Total Carbs 28g (sugar 17g, fibre 3g), Protein 2g

6. Red Rice Pudding with Coconut Milk

The house fills with a gorgeous aroma when I make this rice pudding! You can either make it on the stove top or mix all ingredients, then cover and bake in the oven for 40 minutes.

Featured ingredients: coconut, coconut milk and coconut water

The fleshy 'meat' of a coconut is highly nutritious, providing us with useful amounts of protein, dietary fibre and a wide range of important minerals, such as copper and selenium (both antioxidants), iron (for oxygen transport) and manganese and phosphorus (both of which are essential for maintaining healthy teeth and bones). The downside of coconut is that it contains a lot of saturated fat. Coconut milk is the liquid obtained by pouring from a mature coconut; it contains all of the minerals above, but, like the flesh of the coconut, it's high in saturated fat. Coconut water is the liquid obtained from a young, green coconut. It provides us with useful amounts of potassium, which is vital for the healthy functioning of nerves, muscles, the heart and the kidneys, and crucial for balancing levels of sodium. This, and the fact that coconut water contains much less saturated fat, explains why it's become one of the most popular sports drinks on the market.

Ingredients:
300g red rice (you can use red camargue rice or quinoa instead)
300ml rice milk
1 inch fresh ginger - grated
1 tsp cinnamon
50g coconut palm sugar
400ml coconut milk

Method:
1. Bring 300ml of rice milk to the boil and add the red rice. Simmer for 30 minutes, stirring frequently.
2. Stir in the coconut milk, grated ginger, cinnamon and coconut palm sugar.
3. Simmer until rice milk is absorbed and rice is soft.

Nutritional analysis per 178g serving: Calories 400cals, Fat 18g (saturated fat 14.3g), Total Carbs 50g (sugar 8.7g, fibre 5.6g), Protein 6.6g

7. Cashew and Almond Butter Gluten-Free Cookies

I'm a big fan of power cookies. These balls of goodness are great to fuel a hike, a bike ride, a walk, run or jog. I love them at my desk when the afternoon munchies strike!

Featured ingredient: cashew nuts
Cashew nuts give us useful amounts of protein, fibre and 'heart-friendly' essential fatty acids such as oleic acid and palmitoleic acid. They are a good source of several vitamins, especially vitamin B1 (thiamin - essential for the healthy functioning of the heart and nervous system) and vitamin B6 (pyridoxine – involved in the manufacture of antibodies, histamine, insulin and neurotransmitters). Cashew nuts are also an excellent source of several minerals including copper and selenium (both antioxidants), magnesium (for healthy nerves and muscles) and manganese (for healthy teeth and bones).

Ingredients:
50g chopped cashews
25g flaxseeds
1 egg
50g coconut palm sugar
180g almond nut butter (smooth or chunky)
115g dairy-free margarine
½ tsp baking soda
190g gluten-free flour
1 vanilla pod - seeds scraped out

Nutritional analysis per 115g serving:
Calories 480cals, Fat 26.5g (saturated fat 6.1g), Total Carbs 54g (sugar 10g, fibre 7.3g), Protein 7.3g

Method:
1. Preheat the oven to 180°C.
2. In a medium bowl mix together the dairy-free margarine, coconut palm sugar and egg until smooth.
3. Stir in the almond nut butter and vanilla seeds.
4. In another bowl, combine the flour and baking soda.
5. Fold the flour into the wet mix.
6. Add the cashews and flax. Stir until thoroughly combined.
7. Make teaspoon-size balls and place on a cookie sheet with greaseproof paper.
8. Bake for 8-10 minutes; be careful as gluten-free flours can burn easily.
9. Cool on rack and enjoy.

8. Beetroot Brownies

I've made these for a Premier League football club to show them that snacks really can be healthy! They went in seconds, especially when I told them I added their favourite protein powder!

Featured ingredient: hemp seeds
Hemp seeds are a good source of protein (for growth and repair), fibre (for colon health) and essential fatty acids (for a healthy cardiovascular system). They're also an excellent source of magnesium (needed for the healthy functioning of the muscles and nerves) and zinc (essential for manufacturing DNA and testosterone).

Ingredients:
300g dark chocolate (dairy-free)
100ml coconut oil or rapeseed oil
3 eggs
350g raw beetroot - grated (possibly in a food processor)
200g coconut palm sugar
1 vanilla pod - scrape seeds out
50g hemp seeds
75g 100% cocoa powder
140g gluten-free flour
1 tsp vanilla essence
50g walnuts - roughly chopped

Nutritional analysis per 100g serving:
Calories 336cals, Fat 19.3g (saturated fat 1.9g), Total Carbs 37g (sugar 20g, fibre 4.9g), Protein 7.2g

Method:
1. Pre-heat the oven to 180°C.
2. In a heat-proof bowl over a saucepan of boiling water, melt together the chocolate. Stir until smooth, then set aside.
3. In a large bowl, beat together the 3 eggs, coconut palm sugar, cocoa powder, rice flour and vanilla seeds and essence until smooth.
4. Whisk in the melted chocolate mixture.
5. Mix the coconut oil.
6. Fold in the grated beetroot.
7. Fold in the walnuts.
8. Line a 9-inch cake pan with greaseproof paper and pour the mixture into the cake pan.
9. Bake in the oven for 25-35 minutes, until it becomes puffed and has cracked edges but is still gooey in the middle.
10. Cool on a rack.

9. Sweet Potato Pancakes

I've made these for breakfasts and desserts as they are a favourite in our house and they freeze well. We serve then with sorbet or compôtes.

Featured ingredient: buckwheat flour
Coeliac sufferers rejoice - buckwheat is not actually wheat, but a gluten-free fruit seed related to rhubarb! It's particularly popular in Japan, where buckwheat flour is used to make soba noodles; but a quick word of caution – store the flour in your fridge as it will otherwise turn rancid due to its oil content. Buckwheat is a good source of protein and several B vitamins including B2 (riboflavin – helps protect our mucous membranes), B3 (niacin – needed to release energy from food) and B5 (pantothenic acid – involved in creating cell membranes). Buckwheat is also an excellent source of many minerals including copper (a free-radical-neutralising antioxidant that also helps protect our nerve fibres), magnesium (necessary for healthy nerves and muscles) and manganese and phosphorus (both needed for healthy bones and teeth).

Ingredients:
200g buckwheat flour
½ tsp xanthan gum
½ tsp cinnamon
200g sweet potato (diced, boiled and mashed)
200ml almond milk
Tsp coconut oil for greasing the pan only

Nutritional analysis per 100g serving:
Calories 227cals, Fat 9.9g (saturated fat 8g), Total Carbs 32.4g (sugar 4.2g, fibre 5.3g), Protein 5.7g

Method:
1. Place diced sweet potato into boiling water until soft (approx. 10 minutes) and then drain.
2. Place the sweet potato in a blender with the almond milk, buckwheat flour, cinnamon and xanthan gum and blend until smooth – approx. 30 seconds.
3. Grease a non-stick pan with coconut oil and place 2 tbsp of batter into the hot pan.
4. Cook each side for about 2 minutes, or until golden.
5. Cook thoroughly and serve with the fresh berry compôte.

10. Chia Seed Pudding with Berries

This is so good that I sometimes have it as a breakfast! You can also freeze in an ice cube tray and add them to smoothies for a protein boost too.

Featured ingredient: chia seeds

It's no wonder that these tiny oblong-shaped seeds were a favourite of the ancient Aztecs of Mexico - they're amazingly nutritious! They provide us with protein (for growth and repair), fibre (which cleanses the colon) and omega-3 and omega-6 essential fatty acids (for a healthy cardiovascular system) in a healthy ratio of around 1 to 4. Chia seeds are also a very good source of vitamins, including B1 (thiamin – helps maintain a healthy heart and nervous system) and B3 (niacin - involved in manufacturing DNA); and an excellent source of many minerals including calcium, phosphorus and manganese (for healthy teeth and bones), copper (an immune-boosting antioxidant), iron (for carrying oxygen to our body tissues) and zinc (necessary for manufacturing DNA and testosterone).

Ingredients:

50g chia seeds

2 tbsp manuka honey

1 vanilla pod - seeds scraped out

250ml almond milk

100g fresh cherries - remove the pips

50g flaked almonds

Method:

1. Place the chia seeds, honey, almond milk and vanilla seeds in a bowl.
2. Take the pips out of the fresh cherries and add these to the mixture.
3. Place in a container then in the refrigerator for 5 hours.
4. Flake almonds onto the pudding then refrigerate for another 1-2 hours until firm and jelly-like and chia seeds have absorbed all the liquid.

Nutritional analysis per 80g serving: Calories 224cals, Fat 17.5g (saturated fat 9.6g), Total Carbs 11.7g (sugar 6.9g, fibre 4.7g), Protein 5g

Fermented Vegetables

As well as a fantastic way to use up vegetables that might be going out of date, fermented vegetables are highly nutritious. While living in Japan I often ate fermented burdock root and daikon and our Korean friends also introduced me to Kimchi (a kind of spicy fermented cabbage). While visiting Eastern Europe I became acquainted with sauerkraut.

Sauerkraut

Sauerkraut is made by a process called lacto-fermentation. This means that the beneficial bacteria on the surface of the cabbage, when submerged in brine, begin to convert sugars in the cabbage into lactic acid, which is a natural preservative that inhibits the growth of harmful bacteria.

All you need is cabbage, Himalayan crystal salt and a container (I use a kilner jar or a mason jar) to make a basic sauerkraut.

Ingredients:
1kg green cabbage
1 ½ tbsp Himalayan crystal salt
1 tbsp caraway seeds
2 jars (1 large jar for the cabbage mix then a smaller jar to help weigh it down)

Method:
1. Sterilise everything! Give the beneficial bacteria the best chance of succeeding, so start with a clean environment.
2. Slice the cabbage into thin ribbons.
3. Combine the cabbage and salt – massaging the Himalayan crystal salt into the cabbage and squeezing it through your fingers for about 5-10 minutes. The cabbage should become limp and the juice should appear.
4. Mix in the caraway seeds.
5. Pack the cabbage tightly in the bottom of the jar, tapping it down to remove any air pockets.
6. Fill a smaller jar with marbles and place inside the larger jar to weigh the cabbage mixture down.
7. Cover the larger jar with a cloth and secure it with an elastic band. This allows it to breathe.
8. Over the next 24 hours, press down on the marbled jar to help the cabbage release the liquid.
9. Add extra Himalayan salt brine if the liquid has NOT risen over the cabbage within 24 hours.
10. Fermentation can take 3-10 days at room temperature out of direct sunlight.
11. If foam, bubbles or a white scum appear, just skim them off. This is normal for the fermentation process.
12. Store in the fridge for 4 weeks.

Healthy Barbecuing

I love going to my sister's house when she has a barbecue – she is the perfect host!

Here are some tips to have a safe, healthy and enjoyable barbecue season:
1. Avoid cross-contamination of raw meats on plates, hands and cutlery.
2. Don't grill frozen foods, fully thaw them first.
3. Use a meat probe to be sure the food is thoroughly cooked. (The inside of the food should reach 74°C.)
4. Raise the grilling surface from the heat source to avoid causing a carcinogenic black char on the food.
5. Avoid fat dripping onto the flames, causing flare-ups, smoke going over the food and your guests breathing it in!
6. Don't leave meat lying around. If you've cooked too much meat, cover it and get it into the fridge as soon as possible.

The Ultimate Foil Baking Combos
1. Choose your vegetable
2. Choose your protein
3. Choose your marinade
4. Wrap in foil
5. Place on the BBQ until thoroughly cooked

Barbecue Marinades

A natural healthy way to add flavour and goodness to every mouthful.

Teriyaki:

2 inches ginger - grated

5 tsp tamari

3 tsp mirin

3 tsp sake

1 tsp coconut palm sugar

Mix together then marinade vegetables, fish, poultry or meat. Wrap them in foil and place on the barbecue to cook.

Classic BBQ:

2 tbsp red wine vinegar

5 tbsp tomato paste

1 tbsp Dijon mustard

Dash of Worcester sauce

1 tsp chilli powder

1tsp coconut palm sugar

Whizz all ingredients together in a food processor, then marinade vegetables, fish, poultry or meat. Wrap in foil then place on the barbecue to cook.

Thai Sweet Chilli:

1 inch fresh ginger - grated

1 red chilli - chopped finely

1 stalk lemon grass - chopped finely and crushed with pestle and mortar

1 clove garlic - crushed

1 lime (juice and zest)

A dash of fish sauce

1 tbsp coconut oil - liquid

1 coconut palm sugar

Whizz all ingredients together in a food processor, then marinade vegetables, fish, poultry or meat. Wrap in foil then place on the barbecue to cook.

Satay:

5 tbsp crunchy or smooth almond butter

3 tbsp tamari

A pinch of pepper

Optional – 1 red chilli – chopped

Whizz all ingredients together in a food processor, then marinade vegetables, fish, poultry or meat. Wrap in foil then place on the barbecue to cook.

Moroccan:

5 tbsp Harissa paste

1 tsp Ras el Hanout

1 lemon juice and zest

3 tbsp extra virgin olive oil

Splash of rose water (optional but adds incredible flavour!)

Whizz all ingredients together in a food processor, then marinade vegetables, fish, poultry or meat. Wrap in foil then place on the barbecue to cook.

Chinese 5-Spice:

2 tbsp Chinese 5-spice

4 tsp tamari

4 tbsp sesame oil

1 inch fresh ginger – grated

Whizz all ingredients together in a food processor, then marinade vegetables, fish, poultry or meat. Wrap in foil then place on the barbecue to cook.

Citrus and Herb:

2 lemons (juice and zest)

3 tbsp extra virgin olive oil

Small bunch parsley – chopped

Small bunch basil – chopped

A pinch of pepper

A pinch of Himalayan crystal salt

Whizz all ingredients together in a food processor, then marinade vegetables, fish, poultry or meat. Wrap in foil then place on the barbecue to cook.

Tandoori:

300ml of non-dairy yogurt (soya yogurt or coconut milk yogurt)

1 tsp garam masala

1 tsp turmeric

1 inch fresh ginger – grated

1 clove garlic – crushed

1 small bunch coriander

1 lemon juice and zest

Whizz all ingredients together in a food processor, then marinade vegetables, fish, poultry or meat. Wrap in foil then place on the barbecue to cook.

Honey Mustard:

3 tbsp Dijon mustard

1 tsp English mustard

1 tsp manuka honey

2 tbsp extra virgin olive oil

1 lime juice

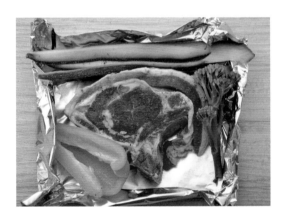

Whizz all ingredients together in a food processor, then marinade vegetables, fish, poultry or meat. Wrap in foil then place on the barbecue to cook.

Snack Time

With our increasingly hectic lifestyles, snacking has become the way we fuel busy days. Here are some healthy snacks to have on hand.

1. Curly Kale Chips

Basic Ingredients:
250g kale leaves
1 tbsp coconut oil (melted)
1 tsp garlic powder or 1 crushed garlic clove
¼ tsp cayenne pepper
½ tsp onion powder
½ tsp paprika
A pinch of Himalayan crystal salt

Nutritional analysis per 67g serving:
Calories 65 cals, Fat 3.5g (saturated fat 2.9g), Total Carbs 7.5g (sugar 0g, fibre 1.2g), Protein 2.1g

Method:
1. Pre-heat oven to 180°C.
2. Line a baking tray with greaseproof paper.
3. Roughly tear the kale into bite-size pieces.
4. Place the kale in a large bowl and "massage" the kale with the melted coconut oil.
5. Sprinkle on the spices and "massage" these into the kale too.
6. Bake for 10 minutes, then rotate the baking tray to ensure even cooking and no burning.
7. Bake for a further 10 minutes until the kale looks like it has shrunk.
8. Cool on a tray – sprinkle with more seasoning if desired.

2. Popcorn

Basic Ingredients:
50g popping corn
1 heaped tbsp coconut oil

Additional flavour combination to try:
1. Garlic and paprika
2. Horseradish
3. Sage and dairy-free margarine
4. Turmeric and garam masala
5. Himalayan crystal salt and chives
6. Nori seaweed
7. Thai 5-spice
8. Black pepper and rosemary
9. Dijon mustard and dairy-free margarine
10. Sesame seeds (black and white) and sesame oil

Method:
1. Place 1 heaped tbsp coconut oil in a medium size pan with 1 handful of popping corn.
2. Pop the corn on medium heat, shaking the pan often so it doesn't burn on the bottom.
3. Pour popped corn into a large bowl.
4. Sprinkle on the flavour combination of your choice.

Nutritional analysis per 40g serving:
Calories 213cals, Fat 15.1g (saturated fat 12.1g), Total Carbs 18.7g (sugar 0g, fibre 3.5g), Protein 3.1g

3. Nachos

Basic Ingredients:
Nacho chips (plain corn tortilla chips)

Additional toppings to try:
1. Sweetcorn and grated carrot
2. Olives, artichokes, chopped tomatoes and lemon wedges (to serve)
3. Sprouted mung beans, chives, paprika and sun-dried tomatoes
4. Shiitake mushrooms and boiled eggs
5. Pak choi, red onion, garlic and grated carrot

Note: Salsas can be used as a dip or placed on the nachos and baked.
Salsa 1 – pineapple, red onion, coriander, paprika
Salsa 2 – tomato, chives, parsley, pepper, Himalayan crystal salt
Salsa 3 – avocado, celery, chives, coriander, lemon zest and lemon juice
Salsa 4 – avocado, tamari, ginger, garlic, lime juice, Thai 5-spice
Salsa 5 – grated daikon, grated corn

Method:
1. Pre-heat oven to 180°C.
2. Arrange nacho chips on an oven-proof baking tray.
3. Arrange your additional topping evenly over the nachos.
4. Bake for 5-10 minutes.

4. Devilled Eggs

Basic Ingredients:

6 eggs

3 tbsp low fat mayonnaise or plain
   dairy-free yogurt (optional)

Additional flavour combinations to try:

1. Shiitake mushroom and red onion
2. Watercress and chives
3. Mixed peppers and parsley
4. Sardines and sun-dried tomatoes
5. Chives and sweetcorn
6. Sprouted mung beans and mustard
   cress
7. Tinned tuna and red onion
8. Capers and smoked salmon
9. Avocado and chopped prawns
10. Italian pesto and chives

*Nutritional analysis per 50g serving
(just the basic eggs & mayo): Calories
88cals, Fat 6.9g (saturated fat 1.6g),
Total Carbs 0.8g (sugar 0g, fibre 0g),
Protein 5.5g*

Method:

1. Hard boil the eggs then let sit for 10
   minutes until they cool.
2. Peel the eggs, then cut each one in half,
   lengthways.
3. Gently remove the yolks and place
   them in a small mixing bowl.
4. Mash the yolks, then add the
   mayonnaise or dairy-free yogurt. This
   is optional as you might just like to
   have a creamy egg yolk instead.
5. Then add the flavour combination of
   your choice to the mashed yolks until
   creamy.
6. Arrange the hard-boiled egg whites on
   a platter.
7. You can pipe or spoon the mixture
   back into the egg whites and garnish
   with fresh herbs or a sprinkle of
   paprika or turmeric.

5. Spiced and Toasted Nuts and Seeds

Ingredients:

1 heaped tbsp coconut oil

Choose any other nuts and seeds:

Nuts: Brazil nuts, almonds, cashews, hazelnuts, macadamia, pine nuts, pistachio, pecan; seeds: hemp, flax, pumpkin, sesame, sunflower, chia, poppy

Additional flavour combinations to try

(NOTE: start with 1 tbsp of each ingredient; then add more to your taste)

1. Tamari and pepper
2. Garam masala
3. Thai 5-spice
4. Turmeric and garlic
5. Rosemary and sage
6. Lemon zest and ginger and tamari
7. Red chilli and tamari
8. Matcha green tea and Himalayan crystal salt
9. Thyme, oregano and pepper
10. Wasabi and tamari

Method:

1. Choose 500g of your chosen nuts and seeds and place them in a bowl.
2. Pre-heat oven to 180°C.
3. Melt 2 tbsp coconut oil and add your flavour combination (approx. 1 tbsp per ingredient – depending on intensity of flavour desired) to the oil.
4. Pour coconut oil mix over the nuts and/or seeds; coat as much as possible.
5. Place mixture onto a baking tray and spread evenly.
6. Place in oven for 10 minutes – turn the baking tray at 5 minutes to stop any oven hot spots from burning the nut and seed mix.

Nutritional analysis per 500g serving (just almonds and lemon with ginger and tamari mix): Calories 493cals, Fat 41.8g (saturated fat 3.2g), Total Carbs 20.1g (sugar 3.9g, fibre 10.9g), Protein 18.2g

Understanding and using the Rainbow Diet
The Rainbow Diet and Lifestyle

The evidence base for the colourful Mediterranean Diet is now huge. It started life as the *'Seven Countries Study'* (those where olive trees grew) as long ago as the 1950s when researchers first compared the longevity of people living on the North shore of the Mediterranean with populations in Northern Europe and America. A further study in the mid-80s *(Keys et al)* concluded that the benefits stemmed (in no particular order) from the consumption of olive oil, fresh vegetables and fruit, nuts and seeds, high fish consumption, but only modest consumption of meat and cows' dairy. Integral though was the consumption of red wine.

We shall look further at all these factors.

The period from 2010 brought vast amounts of new evidence to the table. For example, *Kasterini et al* in a meta-analysis of 50 studies showed that the diet normalised blood sugar, iron and insulin levels and improved metabolic function. This was associated with less cardiac and diabetes risk.

One recurring theme is the high polyphenol concentrations in the vegetables, fruits and olive oil. Not surprisingly, the Rainbow Diet has been found to be dose-dependent: Yes, the more good things you eat, the healthier you become. In one study where the colourful Mediterranean Diet was supplemented with even more olive oil than usual, type-2 diabetes risk fell a further 40 per cent!

Many of the ingredients have been shown to be synergistic too; the more variety you eat, the better your health. For example, several separate studies have shown that consuming olive oil polyphenols in combination with fish omega-3 confers far greater protection for the heart and cardiovascular system than either on its own.

The large-scale PREDIMED study showed that the diet prevented heart disease, cardiovascular disease, strokes and hardening of the arteries. Various Harvard health studies have confirmed this, along with benefits in counteracting age-related memory decline, type-2 diabetes, and cancer, largely by preventing both oxidation and inflammation.

There is an 'ADDED EXTRA' to the colourful Mediterranean Diet. On its own it has major and undeniable health benefits. But as part of a total lifestyle, these benefits multiply enormously. Harvard Medical School in JAMA presented a study looking at various lifestyle factors of the diet. Some, like the traditional family lunches and dinners and sharing aspects were hard to quantify. But they did quantify the effects of non-smoking, exercise, diet and alcohol.

In an 11-year study with people aged 70 – 90 years, they concluded that the benefits of diet, exercise, non-smoking and alcohol were 'dramatic'. People who followed the overall plan cut cancer risk and heart disease risk by 65 per cent. Individual elements made their own contribution:

Exercise: 37%
Non-smoking: 34%
Diet: 23%
Consuming alcohol: 22%

So from now on in this book we shall cover some of the wider aspects of the Rainbow Diet. Far more can be found in our main book 'The Rainbow Diet', or on www.the-rainbow-diet.com.

The Rainbow Diet and Olive Oil

Olive oil is a mono-unsaturated fatty acid. It is the prime source of fat in the Mediterranean Diet. Other such oils are consumed in certain areas, for example seed oils such as sesame, and nut oils such as walnut oil.

The difference between an oil and a fat is temperature. Below a certain temperature, oils become fats.

American heart expert Dr. Chauncey Crandall in his Heart Health newsletter, has explained that eating saturated fats like red meat, is not as bad as originally thought, providing that the balance of oil consumption is firmly in favour of mono-unsaturated fats. Trans fats are, however, dangerous to your health and should be avoided. Equally, measuring an individual's cholesterol level is meaningless, as within it there is good cholesterol and bad cholesterol. The important point is to have High Density Lipoprotein (HDL) levels considerably higher than Low Density Lipoprotein (LDL) levels.

There are thousands of research studies on olive oil. Olive oil has been shown to reduce inflammation in the body – and inflammation is the precursor to chronic illness. Olive oil also reduces LDL levels. Not surprisingly then, studies link olive oil to lower levels of cardiovascular disease, stroke, heart attack and thrombosis. Olive oil lowers levels of circulating cholesterol and triglyceride.

One active ingredient, oleocanthol, seems to reduce the build up of amyloid plaque, a pre-cursor of Alzheimer's. Other studies show another component, oleic acid, reduces blood glucose, and oxidative pancreatic and liver stress.

Olive oil possesses anti-microbial benefits and reduces the effects of helicobacter pylori, which can cause stomach ulcers and cancer, and ulcerative colitis in the gut. There is evidence of reduced levels of colorectal and breast cancers.

And, the benefits of extra virgin, cold pressed olive oil really do seem to be dose-dependent. The more you consume, the greater the protection.

The Rainbow Diet and Alcohol

We are asked about this constantly. The French Paradox offers that alcohol is no bad thing, although there is research showing regular large volumes lead to more cancer. So what is the truth?

High alcohol consumption definitely puts the body at risk, the most obvious diseases being cancer and liver related. Certainly people who have impaired livers should be overly cautious of alcohol. And women should note that their consumption should be roughly half that of men, due to body and liver relative volumes.

'Good alcohol', if there is such a concept, would seem to start and end with red wine. Red wine is made with the wine fermenting on both the skins and the grape seeds. Grape seeds provide powerful antioxidant properties, and in the VITAL study, grape seed extract beat the nearest anti-oxidant by 42 per cent in its abilities.

Red grape skins are known to contain resveratrol, although the more they are sprayed, the less they contain, as it is produced as the grape's natural protection to fungal attack. Resveratrol has been shown by oncology experts like Professor Gerry Potter, in his work on salvestrols, to be a pro-drug. Once inside a cancer cell, it is converted by the CYP1B1 gene into piceattanol, which promptly kills the cancer cell.

Resveratrol is a polyphenol and has been shown to have all manner of properties in research. It improves bone health, reduces type-2 diabetes risk, has positive effects on the brain and lowers cholesterol, macular degeneration and Alzheimer's risk. Resveratrol also replicates the effects of calorie restriction in the body and stimulates the production of sirtuins, which has been linked to increased longevity.

Critics argue that you don't get much resveratrol from a bottle of red wine, but in the Mediterranean Diet the issue is more likely to be long-term build up.

One Harvard study commented that people who lived on the North shores of the Mediterranean consumed on average 4 glasses a day, but in my experience, the glasses are most usually a third of the size of those used in a UK or American bar!

Certainly most researchers talk of the importance of consuming 'modest amounts' of red wine most days.

In www.chriswoollamshealthwatch.com we have covered research showing that red wine reduces 'bad cholestrol', LDL, in the body and another study showing that red wine is actually 'liked' by beneficial gut bacteria. Their numbers increase and thus the immune system strengthens.

A Harvard study in *Cell Metabolism* in 2012 showed that red wine increased anti-ageing benefits, even in the presence of high fat diets. A study in *BJM* showed regular wine consumption was linked to less depression and greater mental health.

Two studies on cancer resulted in a surprising finding. Moderate red wine consumption seems to reduce oestrogen levels and is associated with less colorectal cancer (University of Leicester) and less breast cancer (Cedars-Sinai Medical Centre, LA).

The Rainbow Diet and Spices

Spices are widely used throughout the Mediterranean, reflecting a strong multi-cultural, and particularly Arab, influence. Spices have been used to treat and cure a wide variety of ailments. For example saffron, which per gram is more expensive than gold, and has strong liver-protective and anti-cancer properties.

Here we will talk about just three.

Turmeric

Turmeric, with its yellow pigment curcumin, is the underground stem of a tropical perennial that grows in many hot countries. The stem is a light brown colour on the outside but, when ground, produces a bright yellow powder. It is a common component on the Southern Mediterranean shores.

It is the single most researched compound in the world – with strong anti-inflammatory benefits. It is a powerful antioxidant and is known to boost glutathione levels and prevent liver damage. It has proven antimicrobial powers, often being used in local recipes around the world along with meat that is slightly 'off'. However, these properties have resulted in its use in treating colorectal cancer, and it is known to improve the effectiveness of certain drugs while at the same time protecting healthy cells.

Cumin

Cumin is the seed of a small plant related to parsley but found in hot climates, especially North Africa, India and the Americas. The seeds are boat-shaped and resemble caraway seeds, but are lighter in colour and have tiny bristles. They should be roasted before being ground, but can then be used to spice up a whole range of dishes including curries, stews and grills. Cumin is very commonly used in Mexican, Spanish, Indian or Middle Eastern cooking. A word of warning, however: go easy on the cumin - half a teaspoon is ample for a family of four! Cumin has long been believed to help people suffering from disorders of the digestive tract including heartburn, nausea and diarrhoea, probably due to it stimulating the production of pancreatic enzymes. Cumin is also believed to have important anti-cancer properties, firstly because of its ability to neutralise cancer-causing free radicals, and, secondly, by enhancing the liver's detoxification enzymes.

Ginger

Fresh ginger is often recommended to relieve symptoms of nausea – some people chew a slice, or grate it to make a hot drink. It has major benefits as an anti-inflammatory and is anti-microbial. Preliminary studies at the American Association of Cancer Research have shown that gingerol - an active ingredient in ginger - may halt the growth of colon cancer, and it is effective in killing yeasts and microbes. Research has seen it used with breast and prostate cancer, and in 2015 research showed that ginger helped normalise blood sugar levels.

Variety in your foods really is the spice of life.

The Rainbow Diet and Fibre

It is important to understand that the Rainbow Diet is a high-fibre diet. All those vegetables, nuts, seeds and fruit could not be anything else. And natural fibre such as lignans, pectins and inulins have a number of important benefits.

Fibre is made up of both soluble and insoluble filaments of food. Both are carbohydrate based but neither can be broken down by your normal digestive processes. However, your gut bacteria love them and feed off them, as long as the commensal bacteria (the good guys) are present in sufficient numbers.

Not surprisingly then, research has shown that a high-fibre diet rapidly improves the immune system (by increasing the presence of good bacteria in the gut). A high-fibre diet also reduces the level of plasma glucose, and people who indulge in high-fibre diets live significantly longer than average. Weight loss can also be a benefit.

All types of soluble fibre slow the digestion process, whereas insoluble fibre helps move the waste through the intestines.

Fibrous cell membranes prevent the rapid release of sugar from the cells, but over-cooking destroys these cellulose membranes, which is why (for example) raw carrots have a very low Glycaemic Index, but cooked carrots have a high GI. Whole brown rice is good for you but eating refined white rice is like eating neat sugar. Ditto pasta, breakfast cereals and various grains.

Glucose rushes can have two disastrous effects, for example glucose can directly feed (and even cause) cancer cells and high plasma glucose can heighten insulin levels, which in turn stimulate an enzyme (Cox-2) present throughout the body, causing chronic inflammation.

Dr. Chauncey Crandall and the UK's Dr. Aseem Malhotra have both argued that without this glucose-insulin-inflammatory effect, arteries would not inflame and fat would not stick to them.

Soluble fibre seems to be able to bind to fats before they are absorbed, reducing plasma cholesterol levels. Gut bacteria use fibre to bind chemicals, heavy metals and hormones to them, removing them effectively from the body.

The Rainbow Diet and Pulses

Pulses are very important ingredients in the Mediterranean Diet. They are edible seeds that grow in pods. A great source of protein, they are low in fat and have low GI levels. In the UK in 1900 we derived more than 30 per cent of our protein from pulses; now it is less than 2 per cent.

Not so in the Rainbow Diet. Pulses still feature prominently; for example lentils, chickpeas (hummus), kidney beans and dried peas and beans. Storage is easy for these sources of protein.

Again, the fibre in pulses is an important constituent and controls the slow release of carbohydrate. 2014 research showed that a daily helping of lentils was linked with extremely low levels of diabetes.

It should be noted that soya, in any form, has no place in the colourful Mediterranean Diet. It has nothing to do with the regions around the coast of the Mediterranean.

A word on Gluten - Gluten is a hot topic for some people who are gluten-intolerant. The fact is that they are not gluten-intolerant – their microbiome is. The Rainbow Diet doesn't particularly involve grains – with the exception of oats, although some wheat is used on both shores of the Mediterranean. To fix your gut, you might like to read '*The Secret Source of your Good Health*' or stick to the tubers and pulses of the Rainbow Diet.

The Rainbow Diet and Cows' Dairy

There are not too many cows living around the Mediterranean shores! Typically, the herds from the French hills to the Greek Islands and Morocco are of goats. Sometimes there are sheep.

Let us just stop a minute to understand cows and their milk products. Sadly in the UK, we regularly consume the milk of cows that have hardly ever seen the light of day, and are often kept in a false state of lactation, even eating unnatural 'foods' such as sheep brains (which caused an outbreak of mad cow disease and CJD).

Moreover, cows' milk has high levels of Insulin-like Growth Factor 1 (IGF-1), which causes rapid cell growth. The saturated fat can also stimulate the growth of oestrogen in humans.

One day of high cows' dairy intake sees a high level of inflammatory gut bacteria the following day.

But the case against cows' dairy is not quite as black and white as people like to make out.

Unpasteurized cows' milk contains high levels of commensal gut bacteria (the good guys) plus immunoglobulins. All this prompts a much stronger immune system and there is a stack of research on this in Chris Woollams' book *'The Secret Source of your Good Health'*.

But that is not all. In the rumens of poorly fed mass market cows, a common constituent is linoleic acid, which is not particularly health giving. However, in the rumens of cows kept well and able to graze outside in fields that haven't been sprayed with pesticides, about ten different isomers of linoleic acid are produced by their commensal bacteria. These collectively are called Conjugated Linoleic Acid, or CLA. And CLA is strongly cancer preventive.

Goats are sadly prone to bacterial infections and in the South of France a cull is underway. However, historically the milk of the Mediterranean was raw and from goats, or, occasionally, from sheep. There was far less growth hormone, oestrogen or unnatural contents as the goats often ate while clambering over wild terrain.

The Rainbow Diet and Glutamine

As we have said above, the colourful Mediterranean Diet is traditionally low on cows' dairy and red and processed meats.

And there is a whole school of thought that shows chronic inflammation leads to chronic illness, and the Rainbow Diet is a low level inflammatory diet. Much of this inflammation is a direct result of sugar, empty sugar, added sugar, and refined carbohydrate consumption.

But another factor may well be at play. A growing body of evidence shows that glutamine - an amino acid found in high levels in red meat and cows' dairy - feeds cancer cells, especially those that are deprived of glucose. And this seems in some cases to cause a very aggressive situation.

Researchers from the Centenary Medical Institute in Sydney, Australia, have shown that they can block the growth of hormonally-driven cancers by blocking glutamine pumps on the cancer cells. Cancer cells have much higher levels of these pumps than normal cells. So far they have worked successfully with melanoma, breast and prostate cancers.

As Chris said in his introduction, a 15-year study by Harvard Medical School amongst women found that those who adhered closest to the Rainbow Diet, wherever they lived in the world, found them to be completely free of 11 chronic illnesses. The low levels of glutamine consumption could be yet another health giving factor in the Rainbow Diet.

The Rainbow Diet and Cholesterol

You may have been told to reduce your consumption of high-cholesterol foods like eggs, red meats and dairy, and shrimp, if you want to avoid high-cholesterol in your body.

This is almost certainly wrong.

The fact is that cholesterol is a large molecule and has to be broken down to cross the gut wall. Once in the blood stream, cholesterol is re-formed. In part this can be driven by hereditary factors, but not to the extent some people would have you believe.

A major cholesterol regulator is your microbiome. A healthy gut flora makes short-chain esters. These are very anti-inflammatory but also they prevent 'bad' cholesterol forming from its raw materials. As we said before, measuring 'total' cholesterol is pointless. Each of us needs to ensure that our good cholesterol is much higher than our bad, and the Rainbow Diet delivers with olive oil and walnut oils as a start point.

The high levels of soluble fibre in The Rainbow Diet are another important regulatory factor, be they from oatmeal, or pulses, or seeds like sesame and flax, or nuts such as walnuts, almonds, pine nuts and cashews, or fruits and vegetables such as carrots, broccoli, prunes, plums and pears. These foods contain phytosterols. They are nature's statins.

The Rainbow Diet and Epigenetics

The science of epigenetics sprung up in the mid-1990s.

Early thinking on chronic illness usually held that some permanent damage had occurred, often in your core DNA. Typically this was the case with cancer.

Your DNA is about 1.8 metres long but infinitesimally thin, so much so that it is wound up into a ball in the nucleus of your cells and cannot be seen except under powerful microscopes. The DNA is held in this ball by histones, which in turn are joined to the DNA by methyl bonds. The histones often shift and, anyway, do not cover the whole surface of the DNA. Little 'trains' jump on at certain points and read the underlying DNA, falling off when they hit the buffers. The messages are then sent out to regulate your whole body.

Prior to certain illnesses such as Alzheimer's and cancer, there is a build up of homocysteine in the blood. Under normal circumstances it is neutralised by certain B vitamins made by your gut bacteria. Without this regulation process, homocysteine can cause more methylation to occur, and thus more methyl bonds and more histones. This can cause a blockage of crucial messages. So there is no problem with the underlying DNA, just blockages in its surrounds (*epi* means 'around').

Epigeneticists working on pharmaceutical drugs believe they can break the methyl bonds, with the net result that many chronic illnesses may well be reversible, providing no permanent damage has occurred from the lost messages. The message to date, for example with cancer, has been that 'cancer is reversible - you are not doomed'.

Thus many chronic illnesses are now thought of as being metabolic, not genetic in origin. And here the Rainbow Diet is perfectly placed. There are research studies on many of the bioactive ingredients in the Rainbow Diet showing they have Epigenetic benefits, capable of both 'Protecting' you from illness, and even 'Correcting' a problem if you already have it.

Our book, *The Rainbow Diet* looks at these compounds – research shows that there are well over 60 of them, for example, vitamin D, curcumin, omega-3, indole3carbinol, lycopene, resveratrol, EGCG, anthocyanins, pomegranate and many more. Some will genuinely surprise you.

The Rainbow Diet and Fish

From Spain to Italy and Greece to Algeria, people who lived by the sea fished. Bouillabaisse started life made from the ugly fish the fishermen couldn't sell; salad Nicoise from the anchovies too small to sell.

Fish is a major component of the colourful Mediterranean Diet.

Eating a 400 gram fish provides less than a third of the calories of a 400 gram beefsteak. It is high in potassium, has nil saturated fat and a high omega-3 level. It contains some vitamin A and vitamin D.

Commensal bacteria help fish clear the colon quickly, whereas red meats seem to collect in the gut more readily. Indeed, 2015 research from the University of Gothenburg showed that eating a diet high in fish produced a very different gut microbiome to that of a meat eater. In particular the bacteria were very anti-inflammatory.

Long-chain omega-3 from fish is a fatty acid, which is directly anti-inflammatory. Available in two forms, EPA and DHA, long-chain omega-3 has been shown to turn down Cox-2, the enzyme which causes inflammation. It also has been shown to have a strongly protective effect on your telomeres. These are the 'caps' on either end of your DNA. As you age, or in times of chronic illness, they shorten. But fish oil omega-3 can help preserve their integrity. Hence long-chain omega-3 is associated with longevity.

The traditional Mediterranean Diet saw a consumption of one unit of omega-3 for one unit of all the other omegas (-6, -9, -12 etc.) added together. A typical New York lady currently consumes one to fifty as a ratio. As we stated under olive oil (page 139), there is a strong synergistic effect between these two natural compounds.

The Rainbow Diet and Flaxseed

Brown and yellow flax seeds have similar nutritional values and are also a good source of omega-3 essential fatty acids.

But, unlike fish oils, this is a short-chain omega-3 called alpha-linolenic acid and in the body there is only about 12 per cent conversion from short to long.

This is not to say that short-chain omega-3 is worthless; far from it. Flax and even its modest conversion is especially important in populations with low fish diets. (The only exception is a variety of yellow flax called solin, which provides relatively little omega-3.)

Importantly, flax short-chain omega-3 is anti-oestrogenic and helps oxygenate the blood. It is also very important in maintaining health as it has been shown to reduce LDL cholesterol, blood pressure and plaque formation in arteries.

Flax seeds are an excellent source of polyphenol phytonutrients called lignans. Lignans also act as prebiotics, feeding the populations of certain beneficial bacteria in the colon and stimulating the immune system. Those bacteria also break lignans down to produce plant oestrogens. In some way, as yet poorly understood, these reduce osteoporosis and cardiovascular disease. Populations with a high intake of flax also have a lowered risk of breast, colon and prostate cancer.

Other sources of alpha-linolenic acid (ALA) include edible seeds and walnuts.

The Rainbow Diet and Supplements

Theoretically, if you live your life on the Rainbow Diet, you should not need supplementation.

However, it is easy to think of several instances where supplementation helps.

For example:

1. You may eat really well but live in a non-sunny climate. There is no doubt that 3300 hours of sunshine in St. Tropez and all that vitamin D production must be extremely beneficial. Vitamin D is known to be extremely corrective of epigenetic cell blockages and helps prime the immune system. Harvard Medical School recommends everybody with cancer takes 5,000 IUs a day (that is 4 hours in bright sunshine!) - are you getting enough? Vitamin D deficiency has been linked with a number of illnesses from dementia to MS.

2. If you have been near a doctor he may well have given you an antibiotic or a powerful drug. In this case you will need to rebuild your gut microbiome. A multi-strain probiotic is essential and may need to be linked with some other supplements that can eradicate yeasts or pathogens.

3. You may be fighting a chronic illness already. Most people in this state are nutritionally deficient or toxic. In this case, good nourishment is essential and can be aided by quality supplements in the short term. For example Dr. Young S. Kim of the National Cancer Institute in America showed that once a person went into remission with their cancer, a poor diet might help the cancer stem cells – lying at the heart of a cancer – to grow again into a full tumour. However, she showed that a good diet incorporating the following bioactive compounds could prevent the re-growth: Sulforaphanes, curcumin, piperine, vitamins A and E, genistein, theanine and choline and EGCG from green tea. She went on to say that each and all of these could be obtained in quality supplements.

Portion Distortion

This is my easy, fun and (hopefully) amusing way to judge a portion size! Not particularly scientific but it does give a rough guideline and helps when you're dishing up for the family in a rush.

These portion sizes are mainly for women aged between 35-55 who want to lose a little bit of weight. For the average man aged between 35-55, please use this guideline then double it. The Rainbow Diet has been shown to allow people to lose weight – even when they eat the same number of calories as before!

Soup
A portion of soup should be the size of a cricket ball.

Rice
A portion of rice should be no larger than a lightbulb.

Jacket potatoes
Your portion should be no larger than the size of a computer mouse.

Dips
These are difficult to stop once you start, so try to keep it to the size of a pack of dental floss.

Meat
Make sure the meat part of your meal is about the size of the deck of playing cards.

Dressings
Should be the size of a £2.00 coin dollop.

Pasta
A portion of dry pasta should be the size of a cricket ball.

Fish
A portion to be about the size of two decks of playing cards.

Nuts
A golf ball sized portion will do.

Berries
A portion no larger than a tennis ball.

Storage and Freezing

Fridge storage:

Some foods need to be kept refrigerated to stop bacteria from growing. These include foods with a best before date or use by date, cooked foods and ready-to-eat foods.

Here are some other ways to prevent bacteria from growing:

1. Keep your fridge temperature at 5°C or below.
2. When preparing food, keep food out of the fridge for the shortest possible time.
3. Keep buffet food refrigerated as long as possible.
4. Store eggs in the fridge.
5. Never put open cans in the fridge as the metal may transfer to the can's contents. Remove contents and place in storage container.
6. Make sure food has cooled before placing it in the fridge.
7. Clean your fridge regularly.

Freezer storage:

1. Freeze items before the use by date.
2. Defrost meat and fish thoroughly before cooking. Lots of liquid can come out of the defrosting item spreading bacteria, so thaw items in a bowl.
3. Cook meat until piping hot all the way through.
4. Wrap and label all items in the freezer to avoid freezer burn, and rotate stock.
5. Never re-freeze raw meat that has been defrosted. It is possible however to cook the item then re-freeze.
6. If you're re-using freezer bags, make sure they are cleaned properly.

The Organic vs Non-Organic Story

Food-related health stories are regularly in the headlines. Not only do we all get regular (and sometimes conflicting) advice about what food is and isn't good for us, we are also bombarded with scares and, increasingly, information about the wider health implications of our intensive farming and food systems, through issues like swine and avian flu (which may be related to factory farming conditions).

Artificial ingredients such as additives, E numbers and flavourings, and their possible links to everything from ADHD (Attention Deficit Hyperactivity Disorder) to cancer are of increasing concern to consumers. Connections are being made between the use of pesticides and ill-health. In 2006 the European Commission stated: 'Long-term exposure to pesticides can lead to serious disturbances to the immune system, sexual disorders, cancers, sterility, birth defects, damage to the nervous system and genetic damage.'

Many scientists now acknowledge that by using antibiotics unnecessarily we encourage the rapid spread of antibiotic-resistant infections. It has long been known that overuse of antibiotics on factory farms leads to antibiotic resistance in food poisoning bacteria, like salmonella. Evidence has also implicated intensive farming in the rise of two serious superbugs: a new strain of methicillin-resistant Staphylococcus aureus (MRSA) in farm animals, which is spreading rapidly and transferring to humans, and a new and almost untreatable type of E.coli that is causing large numbers of deaths in the UK and elsewhere, especially among the elderly.

Chris says, "You may think of 'going organic', but not everything needs to be organic – some foods are sprayed more while others actually retain more pesticides than others, so not everything needs to be expensive!" For more on this see our book 'The Rainbow Diet'.

Research from America reports:
- **10 most contaminated foods**
Apples, red peppers, celery, cherries, nectarines, peaches, pears, potatoes, spinach, strawberries
- **12 least contaminated foods**
Asparagus, avocados, bananas, broccoli, cauliflower, kiwi, mangoes, onions, papaya, pineapples, peas, sweetcorn

What is organic?

The Soil Association's definition:

Organic farming recognises the direct connection between our health and the food we eat. Strict regulations, known as 'standards', define what organic farmers can and cannot do – and place a strong emphasis on the protection of wildlife and the environment. In organic farming:

- pesticides are severely restricted – instead, organic farmers develop nutrient-rich soil to grow strong, healthy crops and encourage wildlife to help control pests and disease

- artificial chemical fertilisers are prohibited – instead, organic farmers develop a healthy, fertile soil by growing and rotating a mixture of crops using clover to fix nitrogen from the atmosphere

- animal cruelty is prohibited and a truly free-range life for farm animals is guaranteed

- the routine use of drugs, antibiotics and wormers is disallowed – instead, the farmer will use preventative methods, like moving animals to fresh pastures and keeping smaller herd sizes

- genetically modified (GM) crops and ingredients are banned under organic standards

Washington State University Research
David Broom Research

Food Diary

WEEKLY DIARY				
	Weight and Measurements	Water intake (Aim for 1.5 L per day)	Exercise	How you are feeling?
Monday				
Tuesday				
Wednesday				
Thursday				
Friday				
Saturday				
Sunday				

Weekly Planner

WEEKLY MEAL PLANNER				
	Breakfast	Lunch	Dinner	Snack
Monday				
Tuesday				
Wednesday				
Thursday				
Friday				
Saturday				
Sunday				

The Rainbow Diet FAQs

Q1: What makes the Rainbow Diet different from the rest?

A: There is an enormous amount of hard evidence from research to support it.

Q2: Can a diabetic use the Rainbow Diet?

A: The Predimed study showed that it is a better diet than Western GP's standard low fat diabetes diet for newly diagnosed patients. It provides a much longer window before drugs are needed. The American Diabetes Association even recommends the colourful Mediterranean Diet.

Q3: Is there a need to consult a doctor before starting on the Rainbow Diet?

A: Under normal circumstances no, it is not necessary, but we do recommend that you seek professional advice whenever you're starting a new diet or exercise regime. If you are suffering from any physical or mental illnesses then we strongly recommend you seek medical advice before embarking on any new programme.

Q4: Can anything else be added to the Rainbow Diet?

A: You can add water, supplements and creativity to your cooking!

Q5: Is it appropriate after a heart attack?

A: We believe research evidence shows clear benefit for most illnesses. You should check with your doctor to see if there are specific foods you ought not to consume.

Q6: What happens if I miss a day or have a few days where I cannot stick to the Rainbow Diet?

A: Nothing "happens", just get back on track, get motivated and re-commit to a healthier lifestyle to help you achieve your desired results.

Q7: Do I need to drink a lot of water with the Rainbow Diet?

A: Drinking water is always important. But vegetables anyway are a good source.

Q8: What other drinks can I have? Teas, coffee, alcohol, fizzy drinks?

A: We have discussed the benefits of red wine elsewhere. However, high sugar and artificially sweetened drinks should be avoided as should other alcoholic drinks. I recommend drinking alkaline water, herbal tea, natural raw juices and coconut water. I do think that 2 glasses of Cabernet Sauvignon red wine can be a luxury on occasion though, as can the ocassional good quality coffee.

Q9: Is the Rainbow Diet suitable for everyone?

A: The Rainbow Diet was created for ages 12 years and older. Please be aware that you'll probably start feeling so energised, focused, alert and motivated that you'll want to recommend the *Rainbow Recipes* to your family and friends!

Q10: Will I lose weight?

A: Everyone loses weight at different speeds, but the Rainbow Diet does seem effective for most people. Also, if you need to lose weight then the *Rainbow Recipes* can help if you portion the meals accordingly.

Q11: Is the Rainbow Diet suitable for my religion?

A: The Rainbow Diet is suitable for most religions but please make replacements to ingredients that are excluded from your particular diet.

Q12: Are there any side effects of the Rainbow Diet?

A: As with any new change in routine, you may experience some changes in your body like more regular bowel movements due to the fibre content in the meals that you may not be used to. Positive side effects like more energy, better sleep, less bloating, clearer mental clarity have all been reported by Rainbow Recipe followers.

Q13: Can I do the Rainbow Diet if I am pregnant?

A: There should be no problems unless you are experiencing a difficult pregnancy in any way.

Q14: Can I do the Rainbow Diet when I am breast feeding?

A: There should be no problems unless you are experiencing difficulty in any way with breast feeding or the baby isn't gaining the appropriate weight. Otherwise – it is very balanced and varied.

Q15: I am a coeliac, can I do the Rainbow Diet?

A: Please replace all gluten containing recipes with a gluten-free alternative.

Q16: I am lactose intolerant; can I use the Rainbow Diet?

A: Yes, you can, they are lactose-free.

Q17: Can my child do the Rainbow Diet?

A: This isn't really considered a diet so the answer is YES. A wide variety of ingredients provide a wide variety of nutrients which is only positive for your children.

Q18: Is the Rainbow Diet known to interact with any medication?

A: Occasionally, people may have a medical condition that prevents them from taking some ingredients in the Rainbow Diet (e.g. fish oils or leafy green vegetables, if on the drug warfarin). Please check with your doctor before starting any recipes if you are on any medication or read the notes accompanying your medicines for any food exclusions you need to be aware of.

Q19: Are there any physical states or conditions for which the Rainbow Diet and programmes should be avoided?

A: The Rainbow Recipes are suitable for everyone. Please pay special attention if you are aware of any serious illnesses (physical or mental) that may have an adverse effect on any dietary changes. Our aim with the Rainbow Recipes is to introduce a wider variety of ingredients that may not currently be in your daily meal planning regime.

Q20: Can you use the Rainbow Diet while undergoing cancer treatment?

A: Yes, please follow cooking instructions and make sure all hygiene in the kitchens is to standard before preparing meals.

*These statements have not been evaluated by the Food Standards Agency. This product is not intended to diagnose, treat, cure or prevent any disease.

About the Authors

Chris Woollams

Chris Woollams founded CANCERactive after a very personal experience; his daughter Catherine developed a brain tumour at the age of 22. She was given just 6 months to live, and her London hospital, as excellent as it is, had never had anybody with Catherine's cancer live more than 18 months.

The rest is history.

Chris and Catherine found out so much. They launched a magazine, 'Integrative Cancer and Oncology News', or **icon**, which now goes 6 monthly into over 640 UK cancer centres and hospitals. Articles from the magazine go onto a website which now has over 10,000 visitors a day. The correspondence received is just full of praise. The Charity broke completely new ground in the UK when it declared its aim as 'providing ALL the information, not just on orthodox treatments but on complementary and new, emerging therapies and on cancer prevention too'. Britain's first holistic or Integrative cancer charity has really come of age.

Chris has written six books and regularly speaks all over the world. But he has broadened his base from just cancer. His books *The Rainbow Diet* and *The Secret Source of Your Good Health* now go hand in hand with www.the-rainbow-diet.com and www.chriswoollamshealthwatch.com - the latter bringing research in an easily understandable and actionable way on a host of illnesses.

He is currently launching a video channel and a health company in the USA.

For more information about Chris and CANCERactive, visit www.canceractive.com

Barbara Cox

Barbara Cox is a highly regarded nutritionist, author and businesswoman. She became passionate about the importance of eating healthily during a nine-year stay in Japan, a country renowned for its low levels of obesity, cancer and heart disease. After returning to the UK and qualifying as a nutritionist, Barbara made it her mission to devise a meal plan that would incorporate the beneficial characteristics of a Japanese diet, but appeal to Western tastes. At first she gave patients at her clinic some of her recipes, but, as many had difficulty sourcing ingredients, she decided to set up a company that would produce healthy meals and deliver them to people's homes.

Barbara founded Nutrichef in 2004 and ran the business until 2015, during which time she built it from a small, family business that delivered meals around Dorset, to a national operation with thousands of people eating her meals every year. In 2008 Barbara was awarded the national title of Entrepreneur of the Year by the British Chambers of Commerce.

Barbara now runs her own nutritional consultancy business, BC Nutrition. In this role she advises individual clients, healthcare companies, corporations and sports brands. She also reviews healthcare products, writes health-related articles and gives motivational talks.

CANCERactive

The UK's number 1 complementary cancer charity

Our Mission

CANCERactive aims to provide all people, regardless of age, colour, sex, race, creed or financial status, absolutely all the information available on cancer, its causes and possible treatments, so that they can make more informed personal choices and thus increase their individual odds of beating the disease.

Our Vision

To become the most trusted and most comprehensive source of information on holistic, integrated, or integrative cancer therapies, and on cancer prevention in the UK. We will have no sponsors who could influence the information we provide to people. No vested interests. We seek only to help people beat cancer.

CANCERactive. Intelligent Information. Independent Voice

For more on The Rainbow Diet and Rainbow Recipes follow us at:

www.the-rainbow-diet.com, www.rainbow-recipes.com and www.eat-a-rainbow.org

Or if you have Instagram please follow **@eatarainbow_**

Index

A

Acai berries 6
adzuki beans 6, 94, 101, 107, 139
alcohol 2, 138
alfalfa 7, 22, 40, 107
allergies 40
almond 25, 38, 40, 74, 102, 104, 106, 110, 112, 123, 126, 127, 131, 137, 148
alpha-tocopherol 19
Alzheimer's 54, 55, 139, 140, 149
amino acids 22, 37, 68, 79
analgesic 102
anchovies 113, 150
anthocyanins 3, 27, 30, 51, 97, 149
anti-bacterial 102
anti-flatulent 102
anti-fungal 56
anti-inflammatory 51, 62, 85, 102, 142, 148, 150
anti-microbial 56, 139, 142
antioxidant 5, 14, 16, 19, 20, 23, 32, 33, 36, 37, 39, 45, 48, 51, 53, 54, 55, 59, 61, 62, 64, 66, 67, 69, 71, 78, 80, 83, 90, 93, 95, 101, 110, 119, 120, 121, 122, 123, 126, 127, 140, 142

anti-viral 38
apigenin 16, 64
apple 6, 14, 15, 16, 23, 25, 31, 38, 51, 62, 103, 109, 116, 120, 156
Apple cider vinegar 6, 16, 62, 107
apricot 6, 15, 37, 66, 87, 107, 116
apricot kernels 66
artichokes 6, 7, 40, 107, 135
asparagus 40, 99, 107, 156
aubergine 7, 30, 61, 100, 101, 107
avocado 7, 20, 25, 40, 42, 43, 60, 62, 63, 67, 71, 107, 119, 135, 136, 156

B

B vitamins 13, 30, 51, 53, 88, 98, 118, 126, 149
Baba ganoush 61
bacteria 22, 27, 47, 128, 141, 144, 146, 149, 150, 151, 155, 156,
baking powder 15, 104, 106
baking soda 15, 123
balsamic 30, 33, 35, 37, 42, 43
bamboo shoots 6, 56, 107

banana 25, 26, 120, 156
Barbecue 130, 131, 132
barley 6, 15, 40, 47
basil 23, 42, 64, 75, 99, 110, 113, 132
bean 6, 7, 19, 31, 32, 33, 40, 45, 48,
53, 59, 60, 62, 71, 89, 93, 94, 99, 101,
107, 135, 135, 145
bean sprouts 35, 40, 56, 102
Beetroot 6, 7, 23, 25, 40, 51, 59, 60,
99, 107, 125
berries 6, 27, 121, 127, 154
beta-carotene 14, 45, 50, 55, 62, 116
betacyanin 51
betalain 51
betanin 57
black beans 62, 101
blackberries 7, 25, 27, 107, 121
blackcurrants 7
blueberries 7, 23, 25
brassica 31, 50, 67, 111
breast 15, 47, 139, 141, 143, 147, 151,
163
broccoli 7, 40, 50, 96, 107, 111, 148,
156
bromelain 35
Brussels sprouts 112
buckwheat 6, 15, 126
burdock 6, 107, 128

C

cabbage 7, 31, 40, 67, 107, 109, 128
Cabernet Sauvignon 6, 161
calamari 40
calcium 23, 32, 33, 39, 61, 64, 68, 71,
93, 118, 127

cancer 1, 2, 3, 5, 14, 15, 19, 30, 32, 36,
37, 38, 46, 47, 53, 56, 59, 63, 64, 66,
82, 90, 93, 101, 138, 139, 140, 141,
142, 143, 144, 146, 147, 149, 151, 153,
156, 165
cantaloupes 6
capers 7, 36, 80, 107, 113
carbohydrates 22, 33
cardamom 80
carotenoid 3, 16, 77, 101, 110
carrot 6, 23, 31, 40, 45, 46, 47, 54, 67,
89, 95, 96, 103, 106, 107, 135, 144,
148
cashews 25, 35, 60, 78, 102, 123, 137,
148
catechins 15
cauliflower 6, 31, 40, 106, 107, 111,
156
cayenne 60, 63, 89, 102, 133
celeriac 6, 40, 107
celery 7, 23, 25, 32, 37, 38, 40, 45, 46,
48, 67, 85, 89, 95, 98, 101, 102, 107,
135, 156
chard 7, 40, 107, 109
cherries 6, 25, 127, 156
chestnuts 6, 56, 107, 109
Chia seed 127, 137
chicken 4, 32, 33, 39, 40, 53, 66, 74,
75, 77, 78, 79
chickpea 6, 33, 39, 40, 59, 93, 103,
107, 113
chicory 7, 40, 107
chilli 9, 25, 42, 43, 45, 60, 62, 63, 75,
78, 84, 89, 93, 97, 101, 111, 116, 131,
137
chives 7, 42, 64, 66, 83, 94, 97, 99,
107, 134, 135, 136

chlorophyll 22, 26, 33

chocolate 119, 125

cholesterol 22, 62, 64, 77, 82, 95, 139, 140, 144, 148, 151

cider vinegar 6, 62, 107

cinnamon 14, 75, 80, 118, 122, 126

cocoa 116, 119, 125

coconut 6, 16, 20, 25, 26, 42, 45, 46, 51, 54, 55, 56, 60, 74, 78, 79, 83, 85, 87, 88, 89, 91, 94, 96, 102, 104, 106, 107, 116, 118, 121, 122, 123, 125, 126, 131, 132, 133, 134, 137

coffee 116

collagen 35, 97

colon 14, 15, 53, 59, 64, 66, 77, 103, 119, 125, 127, 143, 150, 151

constipation 100

copper 33, 39, 53, 61, 69, 77, 95, 119, 122, 123, 126, 127

corn 6, 33, 40, 56, 79, 96, 107, 135, 136, 150

courgette 7, 40, 59, 96, 106, 107

cows' dairy 4, 138, 146, 147

crab 20, 40

cranberries 6, 37, 38

crayfish 68

cucumber 32, 37, 40, 71

cumin 20, 26, 46, 53, 60, 61, 87, 88, 89, 91, 97, 100, 103, 142

Cumin 161

curcumin 3, 85, 142, 149, 153

currants 6

D

daikon 6, 31, 40, 107, 128, 135

dairy 4, 5, 138, 146, 147, 148

damsons 6

dates 7, 107

diabetes 2, 38, 46, 138, 140, 145, 160

digestive system 22, 23, 100

Dijon 32, 42, 131, 132, 134

dill 32, 63, 64

DNA 3, 20, 27, 51, 68, 74, 84, 87, 93, 94, 95, 119, 125, 127, 149, 150

docosahexaenoic acid (DHA) 68, 82, 150

dragon fruit 7, 26, 116, 120

dressing 33, 35, 37, 38, 39, 42, 154

duck 40, 75

dulse 7, 107

E

eggs 6, 13, 16, 20, 32, 40, 74, 80, 83, 85, 90, 91, 93, 94, 95, 96, 97, 103, 104, 106, 107, 118, 119, 123, 125, 135, 136, 148, 155

eicosapentaenoic acid (EPA) 68, 82, 150

elderberries 6

endives 40

enzymes 22, 46, 51, 82, 142

Epigenetic 3, 50, 149, 153

essential fatty acids 36, 68, 80, 82, 84, 119, 123, 125, 127, 151

F

Falafels 33, 93

Fennel 7, 40, 75, 107, 111

Fermented 128

fibre 5, 14, 25, 47, 53, 59, 66, 77, 89, 103, 119, 120, 122, 123, 125, 127, 144, 148, 162

figs 7, 107

fish 3, 6, 36, 40, 63, 72, 80, 85, 98, 102, 107, 131, 132, 138, 150, 151, 154, 155, 162

flavonoids 14, 15, 38, 48, 51, 54, 55, 97, 116, 121

flaxseeds 26, 40, 43, 60, 95, 107, 123, 151

folate 46, 51, 53, 93, 94, 119

folic acid 13, 23

fruit 3, 4, 5, 14, 21, 22, 25, 26, 27, 42, 43, 62, 87, 100, 101, 116, 120, 121, 126, 138, 144, 148

G

garlic 6, 42, 43, 48, 51, 53, 55, 59, 62, 74, 77, 78, 84, 85, 87, 88, 89, 91, 96, 98, 100, 101, 102, 106, 107, 109, 110, 111, 113, 131, 132, 133, 134, 135, 137

ginger 6, 20, 25, 42, 43, 56, 74, 75, 77, 78, 80, 84, 85, 87, 88, 91, 93, 94, 96, 100, 101, 102, 107, 109, 113, 116, 118, 122, 131, 132, 135, 137, 142, 143

glutathione 82, 142

gluten-free 38, 45, 47, 104, 115, 118, 123, 125, 126, 145, 162

goji berries 6

gooseberries 7

grape 6, 7, 23, 38, 40, 43, 116, 140

grapefruit 6, 25, 120

green beans 7, 45, 107

green tea 4, 7, 13, 15, 26, 31, 98, 99, 107, 116, 137, 153

Guacamole 10

guava 6, 26

H

haddock 40, 80, 82

haemoglobin 32, 75

harissa 59, 131

hazelnut 40, 110, 111, 119, 137

hemp 26, 40, 125, 137

herbs 4, 7, 20, 42, 43, 47, 48, 53, 64, 66, 69, 82, 94, 104, 107, 136

hijiki 7, 40, 107

Himalayan crystal salt 16, 20, 30, 31, 32, 33, 35, 37, 39, 42, 47, 61, 62, 63, 68, 69, 74, 83, 85, 89, 90, 97, 98, 100, 101, 103, 104, 106, 109, 128, 132, 133, 134, 137

hollandaise sauce 16, 83

honeydew 6

horseradish 6, 36, 67, 107, 134

hummous 59, 60, 107

I

ice cream 119

ice lollies 120

indole 3 carbinol 3, 50

indoles 31, 50, 51, 97

inflammation 3, 27, 30, 138, 139, 144, 147, 150

insulin 22, 51, 53, 64, 80, 85, 98, 100, 119, 123, 138, 144, 146 iodine 68

iron 16, 20, 23, 32, 33, 39, 46, 53, 61, 71, 75, 84, 85, 87, 88, 95, 119, 122, 127, 138

J

Juicing 21, 22, 23

juniper 7, 107

K

kale 7, 33, 40, 47, 60, 67, 99, 107, 109, 133

Kedgeree 85

kelp 19

kiwi 7, 26, 42, 116, 120, 156

kohl rabi 7, 107

kombu 7, 19, 107

kumquats 6

L

lamb 47, 87, 88, 89, 90, 91

lavender 80

lectins 46

leek 7, 47, 107

legume 46

lemon 6, 15, 16, 23, 25, 30, 31, 36, 37, 39, 42, 43, 59, 60, 61, 63, 67, 71, 80, 85, 93, 94, 99, 103, 107, 110, 116, 120, 131, 132, 135

lemongrass 7, 56, 78, 93, 107

Lentil 7, 46, 47, 55, 100, 107

lettuce 36, 39, 40

leukaemia 63

lignans 47, 103, 144, 151

limes 7, 25, 43, 63, 78, 107, 131, 132, 135

lingonberries 38

lotus root 6, 40, 107

low glycaemic 38

lutein 50, 55, 62, 66, 121

lychees 6, 120

lycopene 3, 23, 89, 149

M

macadamia 40, 43, 137

mackerel 36, 40, 80

magnesium 16, 22, 23, 32, 39, 61, 77, 93, 95, 96, 98, 103, 119, 123, 125, 126

maitake mushrooms 6, 107

malt 15

mandarins 6

manganese 16, 32, 33, 35, 39, 53, 54, 61, 64, 71, 77, 81, 85, 91, 93, 95, 96, 98, 118, 119, 122, 123, 126, 127

mange tout 40

mango 23, 42, 116, 120, 156

mangosteen 7

maple syrup 6

matcha 15, 26, 99, 116, 137

mayonnaise 31, 32, 39, 66, 68, 136

metabolism 13, 68, 141

minerals 5, 13, 14, 16, 20, 21, 22, 25, 32, 33, 38, 39, 46, 53, 54, 55, 61, 68, 71, 77, 78, 83, 84, 87, 88, 93, 95, 96, 98, 118, 119, 122, 123, 126, 127

mint 30, 37, 42, 53, 64, 116

miso 19, 112

molybdenum 46

monounsaturated 71

Moroccan 80, 93, 131

muffins 15, 96

mung beans 7, 40, 93, 107, 135, 136

mussels 40, 84

mustard 32, 42, 67, 90, 131, 132, 134, 136

N

Nachos 135

Nectarine 6, 26, 116, 120, 121, 156

neurotransmitters 51, 53, 100, 119, 123

niacin 51, 74, 80, 87, 98, 126, 127

noodles 40, 56, 102, 126

nori 7, 30, 40, 60, 71, 107

nut 3, 6, 14, 25, 30

nutmeg 80

O

oats 6, 26, 118, 145

okra 7, 100, 107

oleic acid 95, 123, 139

omega 3 3, 36, 62, 63, 68, 71, 77, 80, 82, 84, 88, 127, 138, 149, 150, 151

omega-6 62, 80, 84, 127

omelette 20

onion 6, 7, 31, 32, 33, 37, 40, 45, 46, 48, 50, 51, 53, 54, 55, 56, 60, 62, 63, 69, 74, 78, 79, 82, 83, 84, 85, 87, 88, 89, 90, 91, 93, 94, 95, 96, 98, 100, 102, 103, 107, 109, 113, 133, 135, 136, 156

orange 6, 25, 42, 43, 45, 46, 75, 85, 111, 116, 118, 120

oregano 62, 64, 82, 93, 104, 137

oxidation 27, 138

P

pak choi 7, 48, 56, 107, 109, 111, 135

pantothenic acid 51, 98, 126

papaya 6, 25, 116, 120, 156

paprika 20, 37, 46, 53, 60, 61, 63, 80, 94, 97, 103, 133, 134, 135, 136

parsley 32, 35, 37, 47, 50, 51, 53, 60, 63, 64, 66, 74, 85, 87, 90, 94, 95, 99, 101, 113, 132, 135, 136, 142

parsnips 6, 107

pea 7, 26, 37, 47, 48, 55, 99, 107, 145, 156

peach 6, 26, 116, 120, 156

pear 23, 116, 120, 148, 156

pecans 40, 137

pectins 3, 144

pepper 6, 16, 20, 33, 40, 82, 107, 113, 136

persimmons 6

pesto 107, 110, 136

Phenols 3, 93

phosphorus 20, 33, 53, 61, 80, 82, 84

phytochemicals 14, 15, 27, 30, 31, 59, 77

phytonutrients 3, 14, 38, 47, 48, 50, 51, 53, 54, 93, 97, 103, 151

pigments 5, 27, 51

pine nut 30

pineapple 6, 25, 35, 40, 107, 116, 120, 121, 135, 156

pistachios 40, 137

pizza 104, 106

plums 6, 7, 19, 120, 121, 148

pomegranate 6

Popcorn 134

popsicles 120

postmenopausal 47

potassium 22, 23, 32, 46, 78, 89, 122, 150

potato 6, 32, 45, 50, 54, 55, 80, 96, 97, 101, 107

protein 5, 13, 22, 26, 27, 29, 32, 33, 35, 37, 40, 46, 53, 59, 61, 68, 74, 75, 78, 79, 80, 82, 87, 88, 93, 94, 95, 97, 119, 122, 123, 125, 126, 127, 130, 145

prunes 87, 121, 148

pumpkin 7, 14, 36, 40, 78, 107, 137

Q

quercetin 14, 38, 54, 90

quinoa 6, 38, 40, 47, 95, 98, 107, 122

R

radish 6, 31, 40, 56, 97, 107

Rape seed 43

Ras el Hanout 80, 87, 131

raspberries 6, 26, 27, 116, 121

raw honey 6, 75, 107, 127, 132

red wine 4, 6, 43, 131, 138, 140, 141, 161

resveratrol 3, 140, 149

rhizome 102

rhubarb 116, 118, 126

Rice bran 43

risotto 98, 99

rocket 7, 40, 107

rosemary 30, 43, 47, 48, 64, 69, 82, 104, 112, 134, 137

runner beans 7, 107

rutabaga 6, 107

S

saffron 6, 20, 85, 107, 142

sage 45, 47, 48, 53, 60, 64, 99, 104, 106, 134, 137

salmon 16, 19, 20, 40, 63, 67, 71, 80, 83, 136

Salsa 97, 135

salsify 6, 107

saponins 59

sardines 40, 80, 136

sea bass 82

seaweed 7, 19, 30, 40, 60, 71, 107, 134

seeds 3, 6, 7, 14, 26, 30, 31, 36, 37, 40, 60, 61, 66, 71, 75, 78, 79, 87, 90, 91, 95, 103, 107, 121, 123, 125, 127, 128, 134, 137, 138, 140, 142, 144, 145, 148, 151

selenium 36, 47, 50, 59, 61, 63, 68, 69, 80, 82

shallots 7, 107

Sharon fruit 6, 26, 116

shiitake mushrooms 6, 16, 20, 40, 69, 96, 99, 101, 107, 135, 136

shrimp 40, 68, 148

silibinin 3

Smoothies 25, 116, 127
soba 40, 126
Sorbet 116, 126
soya 7, 15, 32, 60, 99, 107, 119, 132, 145
spinach 7, 16, 23, 25, 40, 48, 54, 59, 100, 107, 156
squash 6, 78, 101, 107
strawberries 26, 116, 120
sunflower 14, 36, 40, 60, 137
sweet potatoes 6, 45, 46, 54, 96, 107, 112, 126

T

tagine 11, 98
tahini 47, 67, 69, 116
tamari 47, 84, 92, 94, 107, 108, 115, 123, 126
tangerines 6
tapas 9
tapioca 117
taro 7, 121
tarragon 10, 40, 43, 73, 117
Tarragon 10, 43, 73
Teriyaki 11
testosterone 76, 98, 99
thiamin 60, 106, 107, 110, 112, 135
thiocyanates 56
thyme 55, 92, 106, 117
Thyme 10, 72
tomato 36, 37, 39, 44, 68, 100, 101, 103, 109, 120, 124, 127
tomatoes 6, 12, 23, 25, 27, 47, 51, 55, 56, 68, 71, 77, 98, 99, 100, 101, 103, 114, 120, 124, 127, 128

toxins 24, 60, 67, 116, 135
tryptophan 87
tumours 72
tuna 45, 80, 90
Tuna 23
turkey 45, 88, 89
Turkey 11, 88
turmeric 6, 22, 23, 34, 37, 39, 42, 51, 62, 63, 67, 70, 71, 83, 84, 89, 95, 96, 99, 103, 113, 114,

U

Umeboshi 19

V

vanilla 116, 123, 125, 127
venison 88, 91
vinegar 6, 16, 30, 33, 35, 37, 42, 43, 62, 107, 150
vitamin A 16, 20, 23, 45, 48, 51, 71, 78, 110, 116, 150
vitamin B1 46, 95, 100, 119, 123
vitamin B2 20, 75
vitamin B5 69
vitamin B6 80, 85, 100, 119, 123
vitamin B12 20, 63, 80, 84, 87
vitamin B17 66
vitamin C 14, 16, 35, 37, 45, 48, 51, 67, 71, 89, 90, 97, 101, 110, 116, 118, 120
vitamin E 20, 77, 95, 119
vitamin K 16, 33, 48, 54, 55, 64, 100, 118, 120

W

wakame 7, 19, 107

walnut 3, 14, 31, 43, 77, 125, 139, 148, 151

watercress 7, 20, 22, 23, 37, 40, 50, 55, 83, 97, 107, 136

watermelon 6, 26, 116, 120

wheatgrass 7, 22, 23, 107

X

xanthan gum 104, 126

Y

yams 6, 107

yeast 64, 104, 143, 153

yeast-free 45, 46, 47, 48, 50, 51, 53, 54, 55, 56, 83, 87, 96, 98, 108

yuzu 6, 107

Z

zea-xanthin 50, 55, 62, 66, 121

zinc 20, 68, 87, 88, 95, 125, 127

zingerone 102